THE COMPLETE
BEAUTY WORKSHOP

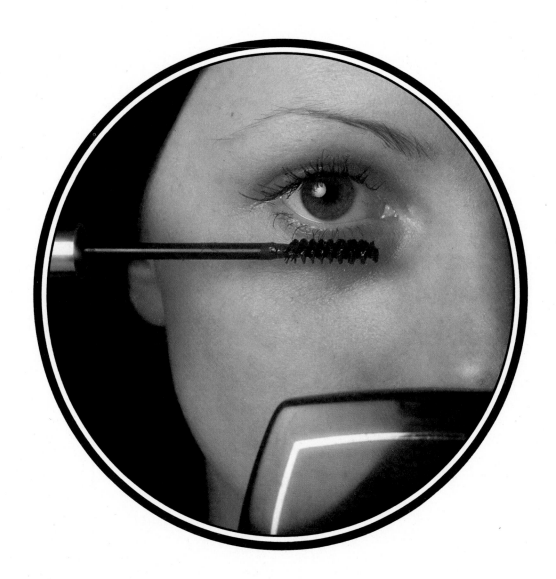

CASTLE
BOOKS

Distributed by
BOOK SALES, INC.
110 Enterprise Avenue
Secaucus, N.J. 07094

photos:
John Adrian endpapers
Steve Bicknell pp 84-89, 90-93
Michael Boys p 116
Michael Busselle p 117
John Garrett pp 4, 12-18, 20-36, 42-48,
    59, 63, 65-74, 76-79, 81-83, 94-95,
    97-101, 118
Susan Griggs p 119

Dick Himmerman pp 6, 8
Peter Reuter pp 37-41, 50-58, 102-114
The Picture Library p 115
Syndication International pp 60-61

contributors:
Pat Alexander
William Breckon
Margaret Stevenson
Deborah Tucker
Arline Usden
Sally Voak
Janet Williams
Michael Wright

Edited by Vivien Bowler
Published by Castle Books and distributed by Book Sales Inc.,
110 Enterprise Avenue, Secaucus, New Jersey 07094

Copyright © 1975 by Marshall Cavendish Publications Limited

ISBN 0 89009 024 6

Printed in Great Britain by Ben Johnson & Co., Ltd.

This edition is not to be sold outside the USA or Canada

Introduction

This book tells you everything you need to know
about making yourself beautiful and staying that way.
There are beauty routines and exercises to cover every part
of the body and to ensure that you are in top shape from tip to
toe. A supple back, a trim behind, firm thighs — these are just some
of the qualities which make a woman beautiful. But with the exception
of a few lucky ones, beauty has to be worked for. Here's how to go about
it with step by step instructions and full-colour photographs.

Experts agree that beauty starts from within. For skin which has that fresh
vital look and a figure that is lithe and supple you need to eat the right foods.
With the special Beauty Diet you can enjoy exciting varied menus in the knowledge that a balanced and nutritious diet will help keep you slim and lovely.

Skin-care is an art — and one well-worth developing. Try our natural face packs
to keep your face and neck looking young, and copy our clever make-up techniques for highlighting your best features. With the ten tips for hair care
discover how to keep your hair in perfect condition and, in the next
chapter, how best to get rid of any unwanted hair. With this book you
need never be at a loss for beauty advice.

Keeping your body trim is no less important than keeping your
face beautiful so here is a unique series of exercises
designed, by a team of experts, to streamline your figure.
With your own beauty workshop you need no longer
spend time in expensive beauty salons
you can do everything in the
comfort of your home.

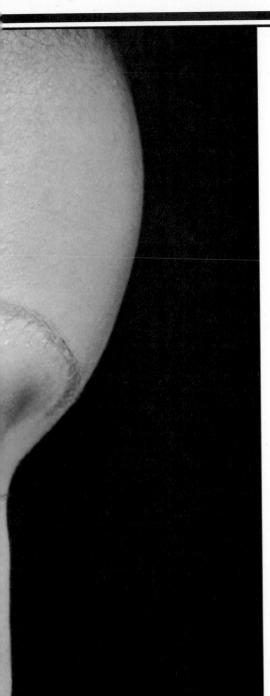

Contents

Beauty from Within

As sales of beauty aids and cosmetics for men and women increase so does confusion, tinged, perhaps, with scepticism, in those of us who want to identify just what are the real beauty aids. Caught up in a crowd at a cosmetic counter, trying to compare and cost the claims of the various preparations which promise to do something for your particular beauty needs, have you never asked yourself if there is not a simpler, less expensive, more permanent and natural way of improving your looks? The answer is "yes" and all you have to do is simply transfer your attention to the food counters.

Few of us think of food in relation to beauty, except in the case of weight reducing. Yet not only do we carve our figures with our knives and forks, the food we eat also affects the health and beauty of our skin, nails, teeth, hair and eyes.

Without a doubt, an intelligent and informed approach to eating can play handsome beauty dividends. And, once you have mastered some basic nutritional facts and learned which foods are most beneficial, your beauty homework is done. It's not like the cosmetic scene, with its ever-changing stream of manufacturers' jargon to keep up with.

Eating for beauty, rather than making-up to beauty, saves time too. You have to eat, anyway, and your three regular meals a day can form the basis of a thorough beauty improvement plan. Consider, too, the money you save. Superficial cosmetics are comparative luxuries, but food is a necessary part of your weekly budget. And this common-sense approach to beauty will also make you a natural beauty and cut down on the conglomeration of beauty aids on your dressing-table.

It was Brillat-Savarin, the eighteenth-century French philosopher and gourmand, who said, "Animals feed, men eat, but only wise men know how to eat." In other words, if we eat well, we will feel well and if we feel well, we will look well.

It is a chain reaction in which the first and most important link is the food we eat—ideally in a well-balanced diet. An inadequate diet can play havoc with health. Innumerable nagging complaints such as constipation, insomnia, indigestion, acne and tension, can often be traced back to poor eating habits. So, if we don't feel well, probably because of an inadequate diet, the second link is also weak and the third link—appearance—will reflect this in many ways.

Dark shadows under the eyes and a pallid complexion can be caused by anaemia, an iron-deficiency complaint which drains vitality and vigour. Tired, cloudy-looking eyes can be caused by constipation which also dulls the skin.

Clogged pores, especially on the face, are nearly always a sign of a sluggish system. Tired eyes and a drab complexion often reflect insomnia as well, while frown lines usually indicate tension.

Most dieticians are now agreed that a diet which promotes health and beauty should be low in sugar and starch and high in proteins, which build and repair the body, and vitamin-rich foods which make invaluable contributions to a healthy skin, good eyesight and shiny hair.

It's very easy to juggle with proteins and vitamins and come up with a simple yet balanced beauty diet. Each day you should eat meat, fish or poultry in addition to an egg dish, a pint of milk, or its equivalent in cheese, a salad, a lightly-cooked green vegetable, some fresh fruit and two slices of wholemeal or vitamin-enriched bread.

Balance is the key word for any good diet. No one food is responsible for building up or maintaining a particular tissue. So fad diets, which over-emphasize one food in preference to others, can

Eating for beauty makes good sense. It is a simple, inexpensive way to achieve lasting good looks.

deprive you of essential nutrients. The best diet for any beauty problem is one which provides meals and dishes made up from a wide variety of foods. This is rather like the formula for a superficial beauty preparation. Even a simple cold cream that you might use to cleanse your face is a combination of four parts—waxes to give body to the cream; a medicinal grade of light mineral oil, which acts as a cleanser, a skin lubricant and softener, and helps to maintain the moisture balance of the skin; water, which hydrates and softens the skin; and perfume oil.

And we can draw another comparison between external skin foods and a well-balanced diet. Just as the skin can only absorb a tiny amount of goodness from an application of cream, and the residue just comes off on a towel or a pillow, so the human body reaches a peak of health and overdoses of beneficial foods are wasted. Equally, of course, underdoses, the results of crash diets or badly balanced diets, cause that health peak to slide dramatically. This can have drastically aging effects on the face and neck and can cause permanent damage to the elasticity of the skin.

Quantity is also an important aspect of a well-balanced beauty diet. Vitamin A and protein are both vital for beauty and an ideal source of these is milk. However, while adults should drink at least half a

pint of milk a day, larger quantities of fresh milk are comparatively high in calories and may contribute to an increase in weight. But enriched skimmed milk is non-fattening. Half a cupful of this added to soups, sauces, custard or scrambled eggs will add nutrients to your diet, but not too many calories. However, reconstituted milk should always be used immediately. Make it up only as and when you need it.

Watch the quantity of food you eat, too. Eat only enough to satisfy your hunger. Try putting your food on a small plate. It will make the portions look larger and you will eat less.

As far as the quality of the food we eat is concerned, the better the quality, the more our looks benefit. Cooking methods count, too. It is sensible to cut down on fried and twice-cooked foods. They are filling, but not necessarily flattering to your figure or your complexion. And there is an art to cooking vegetables. Vitamin C, major sources of which are vegetables, is very easily destroyed. Over-cooking green vegetables, keeping them warm, using too much cooking water or just keeping fruit and vegetables until they are stale can destroy their nutritive and hence their beauty value.

In addition to what to eat and how much to eat, the way we eat can have a direct effect on beauty. The chief need of strong white teeth, for example, apart from regular cleaning, is plenty of good chewing. In any case, chewing thoroughly and eating slowly are good beauty rules. Hurried meals contribute to indigestion and sleeplessness, vexations which are easily detected in the appearance. If you are tired or emotionally upset, don't try to cope with a full meal. Your system will rebel and the results will show at surface level. Just have a bowl of soup or a salad.

There are many common beauty problems which are often camouflaged with cosmetics. If you would like to achieve a lasting cure instead of temporary disguise, a few adjustments in your diet might be all that are necessary.

Skin is the body's largest single organ, and, because it covers the whole body, it has its fair share of beauty problems. Acne is probably the most obvious. The best curative rules for this are to use no fatty face creams and to eat no fatty foods. And that includes fried foods. Pork, bacon, sausages and chocolate, too, should be cut out of the diet completely. Hot-water drinks, preferably with the juice of half a lemon squeezed into them, taken first thing in the morning and last thing at night, are an invaluable part of this cure. Three teaspoons each day of dried yeast, mixed into fruit juice, soups or added to other dishes are also helpful.

A person with dry skin, on the other hand, should eat a diet which includes

pastries and puddings. Remember, too, that weather affects the appetite. It is often easier to follow a diet in summer, when appetites tend to be smaller and toasted snacks and thick soups are not the temptation that they are in winter.

Teeth are particularly vulnerable to decay. They are kept healthy with lots of cleansing foods which scour the teeth and exercise the gums. Soft, sticky and sweet foods are bad for the teeth. The greatest concentration of decay-causing acids forms in the mouth within a quarter of an hour of eating sticky, sugary foods. That's why dentists recommend that we eat sweets and chocolates only at meal-times because, whenever possible, teeth should be cleaned after meals. When this is not possible, the meal should be finished with an apple or a piece of celery or raw carrot which helps to prevent food becoming lodged between the teeth. Another alternative, especially if you are caught away from home without a toothbrush, is to play the game of bubble and blow. Fill your mouth with water and then, by blowing, force it through

Make the most of your natural beauty by eating a well-balanced diet to keep you at the peak of good health.

the spaces between your teeth to dislodge any trapped food particles.

Sleep, fresh air and exercise all contribute to youthful-looking, bright eyes. The eye foods are found in citrus fruits, lightly-cooked dark-green vegetables, carrots, fish-liver oils, egg yolks, liver, yellow fruits, butter and margarine. Remember that plenty of vitamin B, of which wheat germ is an excellent source, will help to keep your eyes bright and help to overcome constipation.

Anybody whose nails crack or flake or break should value vitamin B and iodine. Such foods as eggs, fish and other sea food are all excellent sources of these nutrients. Drinking gelatine, dissolved in warm water and then added to fruit juice, also seems to help fragile nails. For a permanent improvement, the gelatine cure must continue almost indefinitely, but it's worth trying.

The success of any diet depends, to a certain extent, on self-discipline. A chart of what you eat and loss of weight, or any signs of improvement in your complexion, nails or hair, might help you to discipline yourself. Allow at least 28 days before expecting to see results. As homework and to keep up your interest, fill a shopping basket with foods from your kitchen cupboard. Then go through them, one by one, putting aside the items which make no direct contribution to beauty and noting the items which are worth replenishing.

A diet for beauty is so easy to follow. You can enjoy it for itself, and above all, you can enjoy the results—which you can be sure will be long-lasting.

plenty of eggs, butter, oil and liver. Part of the prescription consists of tomatoes and lightly-cooked green and yellow vegetables—in particular young vegetables and avocado pears.

To improve an oily, coarse-textured skin eat bran cereal, wholemeal bread and a salad every day and cut down on sugar and salt. Avoid rich foods, especially the fried variety. Stick to these rules and you will see an improvement in the texture of your natural, genetically determined skin type.

Blackheads are usually associated with an oily skin and whiteheads are a symptom of an acid skin. The dietary cure is to avoid alcohol and too many high-protein foods or fried foods. Salads, lightly-cooked fresh green vegetables and tomatoes are particularly good. And drinking at least six glasses of water a day is an invaluable beauty remedy. It is also wise to reduce sugar and salt intake.

Thread veins are often caused by exposing a delicate skin to extremes of temperature and the food we eat is one source of such temperature variation. If you have a tendency to thread veins, avoid very hot or very cold foods and drinks, highly-seasoned dishes, alcohol and strong tea and coffee.

If you want to have shiny, thick hair, remember that vitamin A is the texture vitamin and vitamin B the colour and health one. Some trichologists believe that good supplies of iron, found in liver, other meat, green vegetables and eggs, maintain the brightness and the intensity of hair colour and that iodine, found in sea foods and many vegetables, will help to check early greying. If the thought of raw egg yolks doesn't appeal to you, try an egg flip. Beat together one egg yolk, a carton of yogurt and a cupful of tomato juice.

If you are overweight, learn the principles of sensible weight reduction before rushing into a weight-reducing diet. For a real figure improvement, it is usually necessary to cut down on your food intake. One step in the right direction is to eat an extra helping of a salad or a green vegetable in place of bread and to have fresh fruit instead of

The Beauty Diet

What you eat and how you look are closely related. Bad eating habits have a detrimental effect on the skin, hair, teeth and figure. A well-balanced diet contributes more to beauty than does any amount of costly beauty creams and lotions.

But eating for beauty is not a one-day miracle programme. It requires perseverance, self-discipline and patience. Cutting out sweets and chocolates for one or two days will not help right a problem skin, and following a rigorous diet which drastically elimates all fats and oils may well result in a quick weight loss, but it will also cause a feeling of exhaustion which will not contribute to attractiveness.

The safest and most effective way of slimming is to lose weight slowly. Crash diets often fail because the lost weight is rapidly regained. If you have tried to lose excess pounds quickly and found that they returned equally rapidly, or that you felt too hungry and depressed to continue, then a slower diet will probably suit you best.

The way to slim and at the same time to gain in good health and beauty is to lose weight slowly but steadily. This Beauty Diet, of an average 1,200 Calories a day, is a well-balanced way of eating that will retrain your appetite to good nutritional habits. It ensures not only a steady weight loss, but has the advantage of being a slow and lasting diet. Therefore the calorie allowance can be ample enough to include foods which, although fairly high in calories, supply the vitamins and minerals and will keep you healthy and beautiful. Wholemeal bread,

We carve our figures with our knives and forks while we eat our way to good health and natural beauty.

for example, may be on the "fattening" list but it contains calcium, iron, protein and thiamine (vitamin B_1) and riboflavin (vitamin B_2), part of the valuable vitamin B complex which helps to keep the nervous and digestive systems functioning properly and enables the normal growth of skin, nails and hair.

Another attribute of a gradual diet is that your tastes in food can be reshaped over a reasonable period of time. After a week's crash dieting, many people tend to celebrate with a huge meal, which includes all the forbidden foods which they have denied themselves. And this starts the "see-saw" weight-gain pattern off again. A slow, well-planned diet which is followed for a month or longer has the valuable long-term effect of subtly changing your eating habits.

If carefully followed the Beauty Diet will result in weight loss of about three pounds a week (the exact amount depends, of course, on the individual). Once you have lost as much weight as you want to, you can keep the pounds off by continuing to eat this way, although less strictly.

This diet fulfils all the functions of sound nutrition. It provides three well-balanced meals a day which include a serving of lean meat, fish or poultry, an egg dish, milk, or its equivalent in cheese, a salad, a green vegetable, fresh fruit and two slices of wholemeal or vitamin-enriched bread. It will provide you with all the essential nutrients for glowing good looks. The beauty foods are evenly distributed throughout the week so that an improvement of skin, nails, teeth and hair will soon be apparent.

Try this diet and then use it as a basis for a lifetime of sound, healthy eating and natural good looks.

Daily Allowances

Meat, poultry and fish
  3 to 4 ounces
Butter
  $\frac{1}{4}$ ounce
Milk
  1 pint fresh skimmed milk, or reconstituted dried skimmed milk (including milk with tea or coffee)
Water
  Drink at least 6 glassfuls

Coffee
  Unlimited quantities, but decaffeinated coffee is preferable
Tea
  Unlimited quantities, but drink herb teas with lemon or milk in preference to other teas
Bread
  The 2 large slices included each day are stone-ground, wholemeal bread

Sugar
  None. Use artificial sweeteners only
Yogurt
  5 ounces, natural and unsweetened. You may add your daily fruit allowance to the yogurt
Salad dressing
  2 tablespoons of olive oil, 1 tablespoon of lemon juice and seasoning and herbs to taste

The Beauty Diet

A nutritious breakfast is the basis of any well-balanced diet.
Begin each day with one of these breakfasts:

Breakfast 1

Muesli
1 oz. Rolled oats, ½ oz. wheatgerm,
1 oz. almonds, walnuts or raw,
peeled chestnuts, chopped, combined
with milk

1 Egg, boiled
1 Slice buttered wholemeal toast

Tea or coffee

Breakfast 2

2 oz. Dried apricots or 6 dried prunes,
soaked overnight, stewed and served
with milk

1 Egg, poached
1 Slice buttered wholemeal toast

Tea or coffee

 ONDAY

Lunch

4 oz. Cottage cheese
Grated red cabbage and carrot salad
1 Slice buttered wholemeal bread

1 Large apple

Tea or coffee

Evening Meal

Chicken, roasted with rosemary
Chopped spinach with chives
Courgettes [zucchini], steamed

1 Large orange or 4 fresh apricots
5 oz. Yogurt

Tea or coffee

 UESDAY

Lunch

1½ oz. Edam cheese
Lettuce and green pepper salad
1 Slice buttered wholemeal bread

1 Small banana

Tea or coffee

Evening Meal

Artichoke hearts

Lean steak, grilled [broiled], and
seasoned with basil and black pepper
Mushrooms, lightly sautéed
Broccoli, steamed

2 Fresh tangerines
5 oz. Yogurt

Tea or coffee

 EDNESDAY

Lunch

1½ oz. Camembert cheese
Cabbage, chicory and cucumber salad
1 Slice buttered wholemeal bread

16 Grapes

Tea or coffee

Evening Meal

Fish fillet baked in aluminium foil with
sliced mushrooms and prawns or
shrimps
Baked tomatoes with tarragon
French beans, steamed

1 Large portion of stewed rhubarb or
1 large nectarine or peach
5 oz. Yogurt

Tea or coffee

Thursday

Lunch

1½ oz. Gouda cheese
Tomato, spring onions [scallions],
 celery and green pepper salad
 sprinkled with oregano
1 Slice of buttered wholemeal bread

1 Large orange

Tea or coffee

Evening Meal

Liver braised with onions
Cabbage steamed with caraway seeds

Melon or 2 thin slices of fresh pineapple
5 oz. Yogurt

Tea or coffee

Friday

Lunch

1½ oz. Camembert cheese
Sliced raw mushrooms, green pepper
 and lettuce salad
1 Slice buttered wholemeal bread

1 Pear

Tea or coffee

Evening Meal

Chicken consommé

Haddock or cod with a sauce of
 tomatoes and onions seasoned with
 thyme
Green beans, steamed
Spinach, steamed

1 Large orange
5 oz. Yogurt

Tea or coffee

Saturday

Lunch

4 oz. Cottage cheese
Tomato, cucumber, lettuce and
 chopped spring onion [scallion] salad
1 Slice buttered wholemeal bread

1 Grapefruit

Tea or coffee

Evening Meal

Pork chops, trimmed of excess fat,
 seasoned with sage
Carrots, steamed with aniseeds
Brussels sprouts

Melon
5 oz. Yogurt

Tea or coffee

Sunday

Lunch

Lean roast beef
Cauliflower steamed and sprinkled
 with grated Parmesan cheese
Green beans

½ lb. Fresh raspberries or strawberries
 or 1 large apple
5 oz. Yogurt

Tea or coffee

Evening Meal

1½ oz. Edam cheese
Grated carrot and raw spinach salad

1 Large peach or 1 large portion of
 stewed rhubarb

Tea or coffee

The Basic Rules for Beauty

Do you really care about your looks? Are you content with the way you look or do you have the feeling that matters could be improved—if only you knew how. . . . Few people are ever satisfied with their appearance yet a surprising number of those people are too lazy to do anything about it. Or have you reached the stage when you've given up trying, believing that it's all nature's fault and should stay that way? But everyone can benefit from spending a little time and trouble on themselves. It makes you feel a better person and makes you more attractive to others as well.

Knowing you look your best leads to an inner confidence—that shows. And it isn't only women who can benefit from caring about the way they look. A smart, well-groomed man will always command more respect than someone who is sloppily dressed. If you follow a few basic rules and learn to accentuate your most attractive features and camouflage

The first step towards making the most of your looks is to take a long, hard look at yourself in a full-length mirror.

your worst ones then you're well on the way to radiant good looks. For women, make-up tricks are invaluable, and for everyone choosing the clothes and hairstyles which are right for *you* will increase your appeal by miles.

The first thing to do is to become totally aware of all your good and bad points. Take a long, critical look at yourself in a full length mirror and then divide your faults into two groups—those that are caused by bone structure and those that are caused by you.

You are, after all, responsible for the food you eat, the life you lead, the amount of exercise you get and how many hours sleep you have. All these things contribute towards general good health, which in turn is reflected in the condition of your hair, eyes, nails, skin and the shape of your body. Make sure that your body has the best treatment possible and your looks will improve, too.

Exercise—A firm, supple body indicates that you are fit and trim but areas of flab around the upper arms, waist and thighs are a danger sign and mean that you are in need of a tone-up. Dieting can lead to weight loss, but exercizing can cause loss of inches. Together, they will not only make you feel more lively but give you a better, firmer shape altogether. The simplest way to exercise is to remember to include it in your normal daily routine. Run where you would normally walk; take the stairs rather than the lift or elevator, and walk where you would normally take a bus. Lack of time is just an excuse for being lazy.

Train yourself into a new way of thinking, and if you still need encouragement, join your local health club, where you will not only find people with the same problems as yourself, but be given specific exercises to deal with areas that are in particular need of firming.

Learn to view yourself as others see you. Both your front and your back view are important if you are going to look your best.

Make the most of summer by playing tennis and swimming as often as possible. Take up an all round the year sport such as squash or table tennis and you'll find the excess inches disappearing in no time. If you really can't face that, invest in a simple skipping rope and allot a tiny portion of your day to it. Gradually increase the number of skips over a period of time, and you will be able to see and feel for yourself that it's no longer an effort.

Sleep—The amount needed varies tremendously from person to person, but on average, eight hours sleep is sufficient for most people. Highly-strung, nervous or introverted people and 'worriers' don't generally sleep as much as more out-going people, but it is very much an individual requirement. One night without much sleep won't harm most people (and you can make up the backlog with one extra long sleep) but constant lack of sleep will soon show.

Eyes become bloodshot and puffed, with dark circles appearing beneath them and eventually skin and hair suffers too. Learning to relax is the key to a sound sleep. A warm bath and a milky drink may help, but if you still have trouble drifting off, keep a notepad by your bedside to jot down thoughts and worries. It's essential to try to relax each part of your body starting at your toes and working up, breathing deeply at the same time.

Posture—When you looked in the mirror did you automatically straighten your shoulders and pull your tummy in? Slouching is probably the most common crime in tall people and just succeeds in pulling the body into an ugly and un-natural shape. If you are tall, be proud

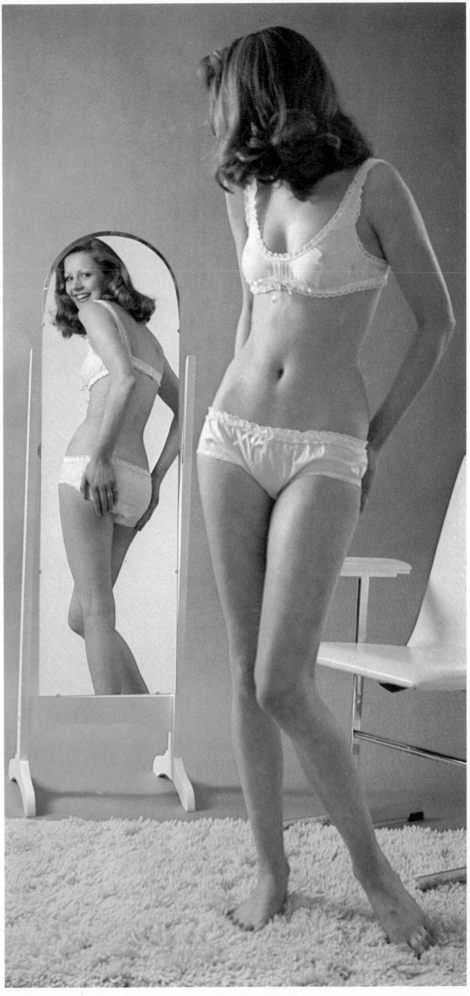

of it. Hold shoulders back and tuck tummy and bottom in. Learn to walk from the hips and practise sitting down and rising in one flowing movement rather than a series of awkward jerks.

Teeth—keep them looking sparkling white and trouble-free by brushing them after every meal. It's the brushing, not the toothpaste, that is important, though if your teeth are persistently yellow, you could try the toothpaste devised especially for smokers.

Brushing teeth helps stop particles of food from clinging to the enamel and getting wedged in cracks and crevices. When this happens, bacteria attacks the tooth, eventually getting through to the nerve and causing toothache. Going to the dentist regularly can help to stop this painful process. He can also improve the appearance of your teeth by straightening crooked teeth, filing uneven teeth and capping any discoloured ones.

Hair—to look its best, hair needs to be kept clean and in good condition. If yours doesn't look as good as it might, check your diet and your shampoo. There are all types of shampoo to suit all types of hair, but the best ones are the ones with a built-in conditioner. Before shampooing hair, brush through first, to remove any surface dust then wet hair and apply half the shampoo amount.

Massage into a rich lather then rinse thoroughly and apply second half of shampoo. Rinse again, very thoroughly, to remove all soap. Handle wet hair with care and pat dry carefully. Remember to keep your brush and comb scrupulously clean, and check that hair has no split ends. Visit your hairdresser regularly for a trim and keep hair cut into a good, basic shape.

Skin—if your skin has a naturally fine translucent texture that is blemish free and a good even colour—then you are more than lucky. Most skin is subject to change, whether it is from diet, climatic conditions or health, and for these reasons it should always be treated with the greatest respect.

Decide what skin type you have: if it's dry, you'll soon know, because after

Picking accessories can be the most exciting part of putting an outfit together, and can lift any clothes out of the ordinary.

you've washed with soap and water, it feels flakey and taut; if it's oily, you'll have an open-pored skin which is very prone to spots and blackheads—and treat it accordingly.

If yours is a dry skin, choose skin care products with added moisturizers and keep away from soap and water only. Astringents and sunshine (or a sunlamp) will help clear blemishes and a greasy skin, and thorough cleansing is essential. Always use cotton balls or tissues when

cleansing and try to avoid touching the skin with fingers. Remember your skin is a delicate structure, so don't pull or handle it roughly.

Hands and Nails—need constant care and attention. If hands look rough and red and nails split and break off easily, it could be due to a number of reasons. Check that there is enough calcium in your diet. The greatest single source of calcium is milk.

Next consider how many times your hands and nails are immersed in water—

Knowing you look on top form increases your zest for life, and gives you an inner confidence that will impress others.

---

their worst enemy—and whether or not you bother to apply hand cream afterwards. Do you wear gloves for rough jobs—gardening, washing dishes, cleaning the car, general housework? If the answer to these questions is no, then start improving them, as from now. If bitten nails are letting you down, try very hard to keep biting one nail, instead of ten. Once you see the general improvement in the other nails, it should encourage you to stop biting nails altogether.

Feet—since your feet have to support the whole of your body, they are certainly worth pampering. As they spend so much of the time hidden away in other materials, it is worth remembering that plastic and man-made fibres in shoes and socks often cause the feet to sweat quite heavily, and therefore a thorough wash each night is essential.

Making sure that shoes fit well and feel comfortable for walking, is another essential. If you don't, you'll find you'll soon be suffering from hard skin, rough and blistered heels, corns and even mis-shapen toes. Give the same care and attention to your feet as you do your hands and nails and then you won't be embarrassed when it's time for open-toed sandals in the summer.

Bathing—having an all-over wash each day ensures that perspiration which gets trapped under clothes is washed away, leaving you smelling sweet. After you have washed, spray on a deodorant to ensure that your body keeps fresh and an anti-perspirant under the arms to help prevent wetness, too. Under-arm hair prevents the anti-perspirant from working effectively, so make sure you remove it first with a special depilatory or razor.

Taking care of your body pays dividends in terms of health and enviable good looks. Meticulous grooming will make you feel—and look—at the top of your form. In the following pages we show you how you can achieve 'total beauty'—from skin-care and make-up to toning up every part of your body.

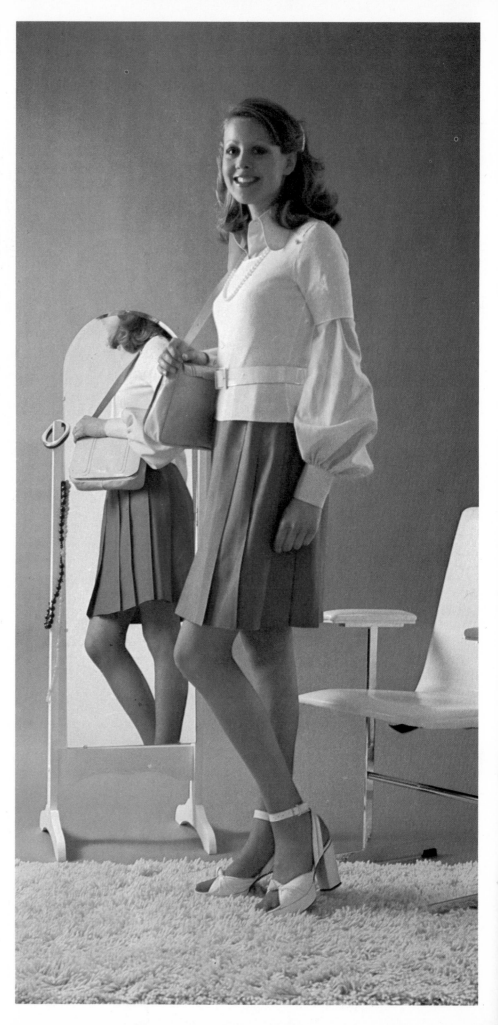

Care for Your Skin

We begin life with the soft, smooth, silky skin of a baby but how many of us can vouch for a finely textured skin by the time we reach 30? Most of us take the skin—the largest organ in the body, covering it from head to toe—very much for granted. But the skin like any other bodily organ can be abused, overworked and fatigued. It deteriorates as we grow older. Whether a person is fortunate enough to possess a fine unblemished skin or one that is just beginning to lose its suppleness and that perfect oil-in-water moisture balance found in the skin of the very young, it is really never too late to start an intensive skin routine. Like any other living organ the skin responds to care and attention.

The most important attribute of good looks is the state of your skin, how you clean it and how you keep it in condition with exercise and the proper food and drink determines the front you present to the world. This, and other aspects of skin care, applies as much to men as it does to women. You cannot alter your basic skin type or colouring but a daily routine carried out when you wake up in the morning and before you go to bed at night will keep your skin healthy and clear.

The basic difference between the average person's looks and those of a much admired photographic model lies not so much in appearance but in the way the two care for their skin. A model's skin programme is not necessarily time consuming, the most important thing about it is that it is never sporadic or neglected. You can cleanse, stimulate and nourish your skin in just a little longer than it takes to clean your teeth. Try it, time it and see for yourself.

Before you start remember that cleansing helps to clear the skin. Most cleansing routines are either short-lived, neglected or performed with the wrong

When your skin glows with health you are at your most attractive. Let this simple skin-care routine help to optimize your appearance.

equipment. Keep face cloths clean and soft or better still use a soft baby brush on your face. Always use good quality mild soaps on the skin. Start a programme of washing your skin thoroughly with soap and water to rid it of the dirt and grime it collects from the atmosphere. For a woman this daily routine removes traces of old make up which clog the pores and keep them from "breathing." Use soft circular motions of the finger-tips working soap or creams upwards rather than in a downward gravitational direction.

Can the numerous cleansing agents on the market help your skin? The answer is yes, but only if they are chosen knowledgeably and not willy-nilly after the recommendation of a friend. To be effective they must be used regularly. Examine your skin in a mirror and decide which type of skin you have.

If you have oily skin with a shiny surface and a tendency to open pores then washing with soap and water should be followed by a light tonic cleanser and then astringent to close the pores. Light creams can be used to nourish and moisturize an oily skin.

Dry skin which is papery, taut and stretched to the touch with a tendency to flakiness should be washed with a cleansing cream or special lotion in place of soap and water. Freshener which is less harsh than an astringent is more suited to a dry skin, this can be followed by a good rich skin food.

If you have a combination of oily and dry skin treat each area separately with the routine applicable to each skin type. The oily panel usually runs down the centre of the face with the cheeks being dry or normal.

Mild soaps that are not perfumed should be used on sensitive skins, gentle skin tonics and water can be used for toning followed by a rich cream to nourish the skin. There are many special cleansing products especially prepared for sensitive and allergy prone skins but

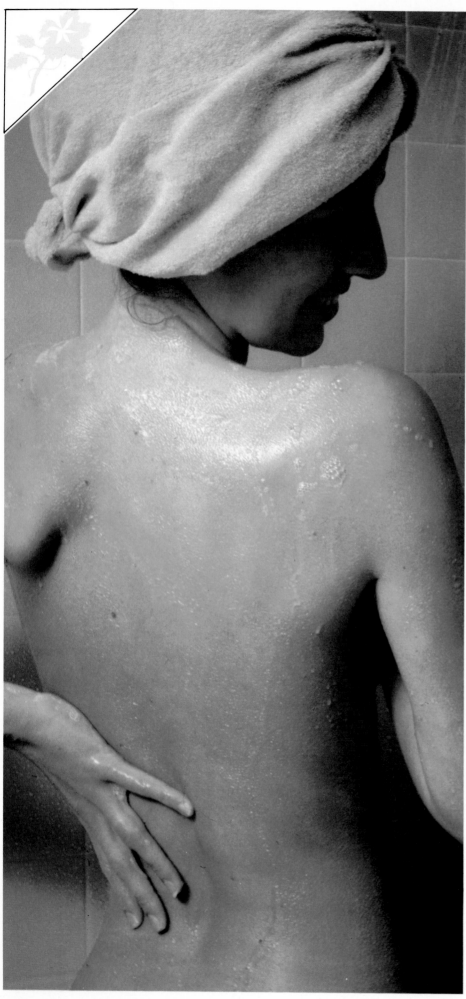

use them on the advice of a trained skin care adviser.

Ageing skin should be cleansed with cleansing cream rather than with soap and water followed by a tonic lotion and generously nourished with creams to restore the secretions lost as the body functions begin to slow down.

The human skin needs moisture to prevent the formation of excess lines and wrinkles. Moisturizing creams really can help the tissues draw natural moisture from the body and from the air. It is all the more important if you want to keep a youthful skin to stay out of harsh sunlight. No matter how glamorous the appeal of a deep tan may be it dries the skin's normal oils and can prematurely age the skin.

Extend the care you take on your face to the rest of the body. Soften bathing water with oils and bath salts according to your skin type. Try to keep bathrooms warm, for moisture encourages the pores to open. You can stimulate and tone skin by massaging your body from toes to chin with a soapy lather. Use a body brush to break down the more fleshy skin tissue of the body. A loofah and pumice stone help to soften hard skin often found on feet, knees and elbows.

Like the skin on other parts of the body the face needs exercise too. The best way to keep the skin of the face supple and prevent flabbiness and sagging is with daily facial exercises which encourage mobility and lessen frown lines and wrinkles. Once lines and wrinkles appear, and they can start in your twenties, they cannot be undone or wished away. But by exercising and learning to relax the muscles you can do much to lessen their effect.

Treating the skin, is like any other treatment only second best to prevention. If you understand how your skin is made and how it does its various jobs, skin care becomes at once more logical and more readily undertaken. It will enable you all the better to make active use of your skin, in relating more positively to the world around you and in communicating with your fellow human beings.

For the skin is a paradox. It is both a barrier surrounding and protecting your body and a means of contact with your environment. One of its prime jobs is to regulate body temperature by reducing or increasing loss of body heat from its surface. Another is to prevent agents, such as germs and poisons from invading vulnerable bodily tissue. Just as important is its task of preventing the loss of vital body fluids. Yet at the same time as it forms a near-waterproof physical barrier, it is an active organ of excretion, helping to rid the body of wastes in the form of sweat.

It is on the psychological level, however, that the skin is a most active link with our surroundings. Quite apart from its role in personal appearance, the skin is vital in conveying the sense of touch. Because of this, it can be considered the principal organ of sexual attraction and communication. For touch, the least acute and least precise of all the senses, is also the most sensuous. Sights, sounds, and smells, can all be highly erotic. But it is the gentle, sensuous touch of a lover that expresses emotional passion and physical desire.

Perhaps the most paradoxical fact of all, though, is that the outermost layer of this sensuous outer barrier of the body is, completely "dead." This only applies to the very outermost layer, however, which consists of flattened, horny flakes, dead cells filled with a material called keratin, which is also responsible for the hardness of nails and hair. The horny cells are constantly worn away, to be replaced from below. Dandruff consists of no more than abnormally large amounts of horny skin that have flaked off the outermost layer. The job of replacing the constantly-worn horny layer is performed by the *Malpighian layer*.

When exposing skin to rough treatment take simple beauty precautions. Use rubber gloves and protective creams and moisturizers.

The Malpighian and horny layers together make up the *epidermis*, the outer part of the entire skin. Below it lies the *dermis*, the really active part of the skin containing sweat and sebaceous (oil) glands, blood vessels, sensitive nerve endings, and the follicles (tiny pits) in which hairs are rooted. Below the dermis is a layer of fat.

The spaces between these are filled with muscle fibres and connective tissue, which gives skin its strength and elasticity. The surface where the dermis and epidermis meet is corrugated. This corrugation is apparent on the outer surface of the skin where it can be seen as fingerprints and other skin patterns that remain unchanged and constant for life.

The skin varies in thickness from as much as a quarter of an inch on the soles of the feet to only a fiftieth of an inch on the eyelids. The variation is mainly due to differences in the horny layer's thickness, and this depends on the treatment the skin gets. Hard wear—as on the soles of the feet and the palms of the hands, especially those of manual workers—results in a deep horny layer of tough, hard, rough skin. Over the soft parts of the body, where there is less abrasion, much fewer horny cells are formed, and the skin is soft and pliant.

Skin softness is related to its fat and moisture content. Normally, the horny outer layer very effectively repels water, aided by the oil secretions of the sebaceous glands. Long immersion in water, particularly if it contains detergent, can however break down these barriers. Then water can seep in and make the skin swell. This simple prin-

ciple is used to our advantage in the remedy of softening corns by soaking feet in hot water. But you should remember that the skin's waterproof qualities are very important in helping it resist infection, while its oily secretions, which are removed by detergent, are antiseptic. It is the removal of natural oils, not actual lack of moisture, that makes the skin "dry".

The main benefit of moisturizing creams is that they replace the natural oils that have been lost from the skin's surface. They may also contain a mild antiseptic, which will help to combat any infection that penetrates the barrier of horny skin, Start wearing rubber gloves when you wash dishes or a barrier cream to prevent your skin from becoming over-saturated with water and losing its oils. Loose cotton gloves can be used for dusting and polishing. Manual workers, too, should take precautions, for the harsh hand cleansers that remove grease and grime also take away the hands' natural secretions. Whatever the adverts for washing-up liquid say, no detergent ever actually improved your skin!

The sun, too, can damage the skin. Even though a tan may look attractive. Individuals acquire tans at a different rate. Until a deep protective tan has formed, strong sunlight can cause severe injury, and this is why one should, at first, sunbathe only for short periods. A good-quality suntan oil or cream screens the most harmful rays, but it needs to be applied thickly to be effective. "Instant" tanning preparations merely stain the skin and do not tan it. Other creams should be used as well.

However healthy and well you feel with a golden suntan, the sun on your skin does you little actual physical good. However, sunlight, particularly ultra-violet rays, kills bacteria on the skin; this is the basis of ultra-violet therapy used for cases of severe acne.

A hot sun causes perspiration even more rapidly than tanning. Your whole skin has about three million sweat glands, forming tiny coiled tubes in the dermis that lead up to the surface. The glands are closest together on the palms of the hands and the soles of the feet. A special kind called apocrine glands are found in the armpits and crotch, and also in the outerpart of the ear.

Sweating is a continuous, normal process. In cool weather you hardly notice it because little sweat is produced. But in hot conditions, large amounts are poured onto the skin. When this evaporates, it cools the skin; thus sweating is a means of regulating body temperature. This can only be effective if the sweat is actually able to evaporate, it helps therefore, to wear loose light clothing for comfort in hot weather.

Apocrine sweat is fatty, and when bacteria that live on the skin get to work and decompose the fatty material, the result is body odour. There are various ways of dealing with this. Either washing

very frequently, so that stale sweat cannot collect; or using deodorant, which both masks the smell with perfume and kills the bacteria with antiseptic. An antiperspirant, which stops the glands from excessive secretion may also be used. The only problem is that by masking and cleansing away the unattractive smell of body odour you may also be interfering with natural body functions and odour-messages that attract male and female.

There is evidence that human apocrine sweat is closely related to the musk that many animals use to attract their mates. Sexual arousal, as well as simple non-sexual excitement and fear, causes a rapid increase in secretion from the apocrine glands. Whether a couple realize it or not, this quite probably acts as a strong aphrodisiac. Deodorants don't necessarily make you more appealing.

The sebaceous glands present a special problem. Most of these open into hair follicles, and since they produce a semi-solid secretion called sebum rather than a liquid, they can easily become blocked. The result is a blackhead. If, as a result of the blockage, the hair follicle should become infected by germs that cannot escape, a pimple or boil may result. Acne is common in adolescence because the sex hormones, which are first produced by the body in large quantities at this time, boost the activity of sebaceous glands, and these almost inevitably become blocked. The best prevention is frequent washing with plenty of hot water and soap. For more details about this distressing problem see overleaf.

Hairs greatly increase the sensitivity of the skin to touch. The slightest movement triggers nerve fibres surrounding their roots to send messages to the brain. The whole sense of touch is extremely complex. It is made up of many separate but closely linked senses, including heat, cold, sharp pain, dull pain and pressure, as well as straight forward touch. It is so complex that biologists have still not sorted out how it all operates.

One of the most intriguing mysteries concerns the different sensitivity of the various parts of the skin. The tips of the fingers and the nipples are particularly rich in touch *receptors*, nerve endings that send signals to the brain, so it is not surprising that they are among the most sensitive areas. But why should stimulation of certain areas of skin—the so-called erogenous zones—have such a powerful effect on sexual arousal? No one really knows, but the fact is that a lover's gentle touch on the inner thighs, the breasts, the neck and ears, and certain other areas can be just as effective in arousing sexual desire as direct stimulation of the sex organs.

It is just one more aspect of the paradox of the skin that the erotic sensation of touch that attracts two people to each other should be so closely allied to the sense of pain that warns of an attack on the body's outer defensive barrier.

What to Do About Acne

The term "acne" covers a whole variety of skin conditions—all with one important thing in common. The connection is the *acne bacillus*, an enzyme-producing factor which aggravates certain types of skin flare-up. The bacillus is, in fact, present in *all* skins—but it needs the right conditions (*wrong* for the sufferer!) to start working.

The conditions occur when the skin starts producing too much sebum, or grease. Usual reasons are the extra glandular activity during adolescence, just before menstruation in girls and in cases of nervous troubles. Usually just enough sebum is produced to keep the skin soft—and the tiny hair follicles all over the skin which have the job of carrying the sebum to the skin's surface can cope very well.

But, once that flow of sebum is stepped up, things get out of hand! The follicles get blocked, and the (usually dormant) acne bacillus gets to work producing enzymes which break up the sebum into fatty acids. These harden, combine with any waste matter, and produce a hard plug which darkens when it reaches the top of the follicle. Meanwhile, underneath, the sebum is trying to work through to the surface—that's when redness and soreness start. Usually, the sebum succeeds in getting through—and a pimple is formed.

Sometimes, however, the sebum bursts out of the follicle before it gets a chance to reach the surface. Inflammation starts, bacteria start working and pus is formed. These "pustules" are extremely painful and potential scar-makers. They need expert attention and should *never* be burst by an "amateur", however tempting it might be to do so.

At the root of these troubles are the over-active sebaceous glands which are triggered off by hormone or glandular activity which is largely beyond control. So what can you do about acne?

While these troubles last, scrupulous cleansing of the skin's surface to remove the grease as it forms (plus the dirt and debris which is so inviting to the acne bacillus) is vital. *Light* medicated camouflage which helps cool down inflammation and makes you feel less self-conscious is also a help. However, thick covering creams will simply block the hair follicles completely. It's important to recognize the degree of your acne condition. Do you for instance have:

Greasy, shiny facial skin and blackheads? Treat the condition yourself, with regular and thorough cleansing (using medicated pads during the day if you can't get to a *clean* cloakroom), and by wearing a light, medicated make-up.

You can remove blackheads yourself, using a *comedo-expressor*—a spoon-shaped instrument with a hole in the bowl. First, place a hot compress over the blackhead area, then place the sterilized expressor over each blackhead in turn and use a gently rocking movement to squeeze it out. If you're ham-fisted it's best to leave it alone. And if the blackheads are in difficult spots like your ears and the back of your neck, then go to a beauty specialist.

Greasy skin, blackheads and spots? Proceed as above, but use a drying medicated cream on the spots at night. Watch for the pustules. If you get one or two, leave them alone. If a lot start—consult your doctor.

Pustules, spots and blackheads? If you have all three types of acne erupting anywhere on your skin (face or body) then do see your doctor. He will give excellent advice and prescribe the right treatment. Never try to cope with this kind of acne alone. By getting the right treatment *now*, the condition can be checked before there's any danger of scarring.

The A-Z of Acne

Acidity Fatty acids on the skin's surface combine with dead cells and waste matter to form blackheads and whiteheads. *Over*-acidity can be one of the contributory factors to acne.

Androgen This is the male sex hormone (secreted by women too, but to a lesser degree) which can cause oversecretion of skin sebum during adolescence.

Blackheads Caused when too much sebum tries to force its way through the tiny hair follicles on the face, chest and back. The acne bacillus breaks up the sebum into irritant fatty acids (see A), which combine with dead cells and waste matter to form a horny plug. On exposure to the air, oxidation takes place and the plug turns black. Blackheads are called "comedos" by dermatologists.

Cleansing Removing the extra grease on the skin is a vital part of acne treatment. Cleanse *at least* three times a day using a non-irritant soap or liquid preparation.

Camouflage Heavy grease-based make-up may cover acne—but it will certainly aggravate the condition. However, a light, medicated make-up can help in two ways:

it effectively camouflages the condition; and increased confidence means less nervous tension and this can help to calm down those over-active sebaceous glands.

Dermatologist If your acne condition is persistent a visit to a skin specialist, or dermatologist, can be a good idea.

Epidermis This is the top layer of the complex, multi-layer structure of skin. It's composed of over-lapping flat cells of an insoluble protein called keratin. The cells are continually replaced from plump, live cells in the lower layers of the skin and "rubbed off" at the top. Total life-span of a cell from start to finish is about one month.

Food Diet can help skin troubles considerably, since every cell in the body (including those involved in skin health) are formulated from the substances we eat—proteins, vitamins, minerals. Chocolate and fried food won't themselves irritate an acne condition—but don't eat them at the expense of foods which actually help formulate healthy skin.

You need: fresh fruit (especially citrus fruit), vegetables, dairy foods, meat or fish and plenty of water to keep elimination regular.

You don't need: sugar, and sugar-based foods, starchy foods, alcohol, excess of coffee, tea.

Grease glands "Greasy skin" is caused by over-active sebaceous glands which, in turn, can be triggered off by other factors. The greasy area can be all over the face, chest and back or confined to specific zones such as nose, chin, forehead. However, a certain amount of sebum is *essential* to soften the keratin layer which forms the epidermis, or outer-skin. One bonus—a greasy skin is less prone to wrinkles later on than a dry one!

Hair Oily hair often goes with an acne condition. Even if you don't suffer from dandruff, strands of hair falling onto the face can aggravate acne by causing a build-up of grease and dirt. Hair should be kept *off* the face and shampooed regularly.

Infection Rigorous skin-care is necessary to keep irritant factors (grease, dirt and flaky skin) at bay, *not* to prevent spreading. "If you touch that spot, it'll spread," say well-intentioned advisors. It won't—but it will be irritated and possibly take longer to heal, especially if bacteria are present.

Jobs Working in a hot atmosphere (bakery, over-heated office, factory) or in a job which involves heavy physical activity means *perspiration* is likely. This will give the narrow hair-follicles in the skin even more work to do—and will aggravate acne. The only solution is to *wash*—thoroughly and carefully—whenever there's an opportunity. Another idea is to mop your face with fresh medicated cleansing pads at regular intervals. *Don't* use a handkerchief.

Keratin This is the horny, protein-based substance which forms the top layer of the skin. It's also the stuff that toenails, fingernails and hair are made of. A high-protein diet (meat, eggs, fish, cheese) helps replace dead keratin cells.

Knowledge Learn all you can about *your* skin—and use the knowledge wisely.

Loofah Scrubbing a greasy, acne-prone back with a clean loofah will whisk away dead cells. Not recommended, though, where spots, pustules and blackheads are sore and inflamed.

Laxative Irregular bowel movements usually indicate irregular meals with insufficient roughage (bread, green vegetables, fruit). By taking a laxative, you're attacking the symptom, not the cause. Instead, regulate diet and mealtimes and drink lots of water.

Menstruation Pre-menstrual glandular activity (producing androgen again) often gives girls a mild kind of acne during the days before the menstrual period starts. Minimize the problem by keeping skin scrupulously clean during this time.

Medication Patent acne creams can help in cleansing and healing inflamed acne conditions. However, to get the product which is absolutely right for *you*, consult your doctor. He may also recommend a course of antibiotics.

Nerves Nervous tension can certainly make acne worse. Try not to let the situation get you down.

Oily creams Avoid any make-up with an oil base. Even if you like to remove eye make-up with baby oil, make sure that none goes onto the skin of your cheeks or forehead. Avoid too much oily food or salad dressings.

Pustules These are dangerous, and occur when the grease and debris blocking the hair follicle gets *really* out of hand. The follicle wall breaks, the fatty acids spread under the skin and pus is formed. Never try to squeeze these—it's a job for an expert. If you do, scarring can result.

Puberty Danger time for acne. Skin secretions are stepped up because of heightened glandular activity—more pronounced in boys than girls. The end of puberty usually eases the situation.

Peeling Removal of extra layers of the epidermis with the object of encouraging rapid fresh cell growth. Peeling "agents" are usually chemical compounds based on sulphur or resorcinol. The process is usually carried out by a beauty therapist or dermatologist.

Questions *Ask* your doctor and dermatologist as many questions as you like —they'll be delighted to answer them. Don't be too shy or embarrassed to discuss your problems.

Redness, roughness Avoid wearing scratchy clothing which could irritate your skin: woollen jerseys should be as soft as possible—and the same goes for underwear. It's best to wear *cotton* underwear if you have acne on back, chest or buttocks, as synthetic fabrics do not absorb perspiration.

Scars If you try to squeeze acne spots yourself (especially the "blind" pustules), you could get scarring. Even blackheads should only be extracted with the greatest care. However, bad scarring can be helped by cosmetic surgery.

Touching Don't. Easier said than done? Yes, but fiddling with spots will simply bruise and redden an area which is sensitive enough already. Knit, crochet, draw, paint, or take up carpentry in the evening—anything to keep those hands occupied!

Ugly Your skin condition probably doesn't make you look as bad as you think. In any case, with the right treatment, things will probably improve very soon. Meantime, play up your *good* points—hair, eyes, nails, figure, personality, know-how.

Vitamins Vitamin C from oranges, grapefruit, fresh-cooked green vegetables, helps to purify and vitalize the blood stream. Next come Vitamins A (yellow foods) and B_2 in liver, kidneys, milk, fruit and vegetables, Keep off those gooey cakes and sweets.

Whiteheads These are little bead-like plugs in the hair follicles—like blackheads, but with a thin layer of skin on top which prevents the oxidation process which turns them black. Often found near eyes and upper cheeks, singly or in groups. Don't try to remove them yourself, as the skin must be pierced before the matter is extracted. Consult your doctor or qualified beauty therapist.

Washing Use non-irritant soap when washing spotty skin. Blackheads and dead cells can be removed by *gentle* circular brushing movements with a soft, clean brush. Not for really spotty areas, though.

X marks the spot As acne spots and blackheads start to disappear, don't neglect skin care. If you've had acne, you need to be doubly vigilant about cleaning your skin thoroughly and removing dirt or stale make-up.

Yashmak Hiding a problem never solved it!

Zeal Your secret weapon in the war on acne. Keep up the good work!

Answers to Questions on Acne

Is it catching?
No. Acne is a glandular complaint—not an infection. You can't give it to your friends by touching or kissing. However, bacteria on the skin's surface can certainly irritate the condition for you— that's why regular, thorough cleansing is essential.

Does long hair aggravate acne?
The same circumstances that are producing too much sebum in your skin, may also produce too much sebum in the hair follicles on your head—that's why greasy hair and, occasionally, dandruff go hand-in-hand with acne. If grease from the hair is allowed to touch the skin, this will certainly cause a build-up of dirt, oil and bacteria which will inflame the spots. Keep hair very clean with a medicated shampoo—and keep it *off* your face. However, if acne spots are not present on the neck, there's no reason for cutting

hair really short. But avoid fringes, side-curls, long sideboards and floppy fronds which continually touch the face.

Should I use an astringent to close open pores?
Cleanse face thoroughly at night, and splash with a little cold water. A harsh astringent which artificially closes pores will actually prevent excess sebum escaping naturally through hair follicles and could make your acne worse. It's better to wake up with a shiny face in the morning—and wash off the grease and dirt straight away!

Is acne an allergy?
No. It is always the result of glandular and hormonal activity.

Does it automatically disappear at the end of adolescence?
Not necessarily. Glandular activity can go on right into the twenties. Dramatic bodily changes like pregnancy can also bring a crop of acne spots on face, back or chest. But the most *likely* time for bad acne is during the teens. The vast majority of cases improve dramatically then disappear altogether in the early twenties.

Does it run in families?
Yes—over-active sebaceous glands can be a family tendency. However, like over-weight, some can be attributed to family *habits* as well as inherited physical traits. If thorough washing isn't exactly a family habit—then it should be. Similarly, if you are brought up with a diet that contains insufficient vitamin C—skin troubles can result.

How common is it?
Very. Most boys and the vast majority of girls experience some form of skin trouble in puberty. So don't think *you* are a lone sufferer!

Does eating chocolate make it worse?
No. Chocolate and fried foods are no longer thought to aggravate acne. However, where these foods are eaten in preference to those which actually help to provide the minerals and vitamins which form healthy skin, trouble can start. But this is due to an *insufficiency* of the "good" foods, rather than too many of the "bad". However, chocolate, fried foods and starch will certainly help make you fat—and sugary foods will hasten dental decay—and surely one problem is enough for now?

Can I insist on seeing a dermatologist?
First, do try the remedies suggested by your doctor. Then, you can certainly suggest that a visit to a dermatologist might help. Many young acne sufferers are "doctor-resistant" to extremes. Don't be. Give him a chance—and listen to his advice.

Does masturbation cause acne?
No—this is an old wives' tale.

Will sunshine help clear it up?
Strong sunshine which tans the skin (or an ultra-violet lamp) will disguise the condition and help dry up the grease—but it won't cure acne. If you perspire heavily while sunbathing, you'll make things worse.

Beauty Treatments from the Earth

Few people realize that a great source of facial beauty lies in their natural surroundings. The earth you walk upon can be used to keep your skin clean, oil-free and young. If you regularly use these various face masks you can have a glowing, healthy complexion free from blemishes. It is never too early to start caring for your skin and insuring that it will always look youthful.

Ever since the fashionable Egyptians pounded ants' eggs to use as eye ointment and the Romans covered themselves with castor oil extract to soften and beautify their skin, women and men have searched for substances to enhance their beauty. Their searches have led them to things around them—trees, plants, animal substances—and the earth itself.

The pursuit of cosmetic art sometimes produced strange and even dangerous results. In the eighteenth century many fashionable ladies ruined their skins by painting themselves with white lead paint. Lead is now known to be a highly toxic substance. In the same century it was a common practice to cover children's hair with walnut oil. The oil was supposed to decrease the growth of hair and produce the fashionable high forehead. If that did not work, people would often resort to quick lime as an alternative. Unfortunately, of course, the lime also removed whole patches of skin.

Lotions, bath additives and face-packs based on gentler natural substances from the earth are now used all round the world in beauty salons and health farms. Some of the recipes have been handed down through the centuries. They had been seen to work; chemists and biochemists can now tell us why they work. Minerals and vitamins can often improve skin tone, colour and texture from the outside as well as the inside. And favourite ingredients for beauty treatments—Fuller's earth, kaolin, brewer's yeast, oatmeal and peat—are rich in these.

When put on your skin these substances can make a tremendous difference to your appearance. The recipes for these face-packs and baths should be followed carefully and should be used regularly. It will not take long for you to notice a definite improvement in the texture and health of your skin.

All the treatments must, however, be used with care. Although they are all natural the ingredients can have a powerful effect. For example, do not try to give yourself a Fuller's earth mask if you have dry, difficult skin. The absorbent properties of this substance are so powerful that it can be used to clean grease spots on fabric. If you imagine that kind of process occurring on top of your skin you will understand how powerful the action is. If you are allergic to anti-perspirants then do not use Fuller's earth or kaolin because they contain the aluminium salts—also added to anti-perspirants—which are likely to be the cause of your allergy.

When you have mixed a mask, always try out the effect on the inside of your wrist before applying it to your face. Take the precaution of tying your hair back with a ribbon and placing a towel around your shoulders before you start. Make sure you are unlikely to be disturbed, too, as some of the mixtures can look very strange to an observer.

The ingredients in these packs vary so it is best to try out a few and discover which one is the most beneficial to your skin.

Fuller's earth is a special kind of clay which possesses highly absorbent qualities. It was originally used in the 'fulling' (cleansing) of cloth. It is rich in minerals and when applied to the skin in the form of a paste it helps improve circulation. It hardens slowly as it dries, absorbing the dead cells on the top of the skin, and drying up any excessive oil.

The mineral ingredient in Fuller's earth which gives it this absorbent action is hydrated aluminium silicate. (This is used in modern anti-perspirants.) Grease in the skin coats the particles of aluminium silicate and is lifted away from the skin when the earth is removed. It is, therefore, unsuitable for a very dry skin but excellent for an oily or spotty one.

Use just one tablespoon of powdered earth to one tablespoon of warm water. (It is also available at chemists in cream form.) Apply to the skin, avoiding the delicate area around the eyes, and leave on for about 20 minutes or until completely dry. Rinse off with warm water. The result is a clear, pinkish skin—the pink tinge is caused by the stepping up of blood circulation just below the surface —with all excess grease and dead cells cleared away. The treatment should be used once a week, or twice a week for very oily skins.

For anyone with a perspiration problem Fuller's earth makes a very good absorbent foot-powder when it is mixed with talc. The earth and talc mixture can be sprinkled into shoes or rubbed directly on to the feet.

Fuller's earth is also effective as an emergency dry shampoo. Sprinkle a little earth over the hair, rub in well and leave for about 15 minutes. Brush out with a firm, clean bristle brush. The grease will have been absorbed, leaving the hair clean and shining.

Kaolin is a fine clay, greyish in colour, which is used to make delicate pottery. It is formed in the earth by the decomposition of felspar, a group of materials which probably make up more than half of the earth's crust. Although felspar is very common, the conditions for formation of kaolin itself are only right in relatively few places—China, Japan, Devon and Cornwall in England, Limoges in France and some parts of the United States.

Kaolin has long been used as a treatment for infections. When applied externally the minerals combine to give a 'drawing' action, removing toxins. Taken internally, kaolin removes toxins from the system and helps to relieve stomach upsets. In the same way, kaolin can remove grime and dead cells from the complexion. The action is, however, astringent so kaolin alone is not suitable for dry skins.

To make a face mask mix one tablespoon of kaolin with a little water to make a moderately thick paste. Cleanse the skin, apply the paste and leave to dry (about 5-10 minutes), then rinse off with warm water. The skin should be fresher, whiter and cleaner than before.

A slightly gentler face mask is particularly good for sallow, tired-looking skins with or without blackheads and other blemishes. Make it by mixing two ounces of kaolin with half a teaspoon each of rosewater, glycerine and tincture of Benzoin. (This last is a balsamic resin obtained from trees growing in Sumatra and Java.) Apply the mask with the fingers or with cotton wool, leave it to dry for 30 minutes, then wash it off with warm water. The skin becomes soft and smooth with a glowing colour.

Peat and Mud have been associated with beauty and health for many centuries. The fashionable ladies of the eighteenth and nineteenth centuries made yearly pilgrimages to the sulphur-rich black mud baths of Germany, France and Austria. In addition to overcoming fatigue and cleansing the skin the highly-concentrated mineral-rich substances were reputed to help cure rheumatism and arthritis and even

A Fuller's earth face pack is rich in minerals and helps improve circulation. It is excellent for oily skin as it absorbs all surface grease and leaves the skin clear and glowing, with a pinkish tinge.

believed to slim overweight beauties.

The rich deposits of peat and mud are formed by complicated processes of decomposition of plants and herbs which have been going on for thousands of years. Peat, in fact, is decayed vegetable matter—coal in its first stage of development. It is found in marshy places and is common in Ireland and Scotland, although the peat found there is used for fuel not beauty treatments.

In upper Austria, however, at Neydharting, there is a rich deposit which has been used as a cosmetic aid for several centuries. The analysis of this moor peat shows that it contains minerals such as potassium, magnesium, sulphur and calcium together with essential oils, fats and lipids—substances which are often added artificially to man-made cosmetics. The Neydharting peat can be used as a mask to cleanse, tone and protect the skin, leaving it silky smooth. It appears to be effective in the treatment of skin blemishes and acne.

Many health farms and beauty salons offer mud and peat bath treatments for all-over beauty. These definitely need professional beauticians and specialised equipment for practical application. It would be extremely difficult, for example, to obtain enough spa mud to use at home. The treatment itself could be rather messy, as well. However, many pharmacies and health food stores stock peat bath additives and face packs which are easy to apply at home.

Oatmeal is very close to the earth because it is made from one of man's basic food ingredients—oats. As well as being a staple food oatmeal has marvellous properties as a facial beauty treatment. It is rich in vitamin B, which when taken internally keeps skin healthy, and vitamin E, reputed to be an anti-aging factor. Many cosmetics manufacturers are now including vitamin E in their

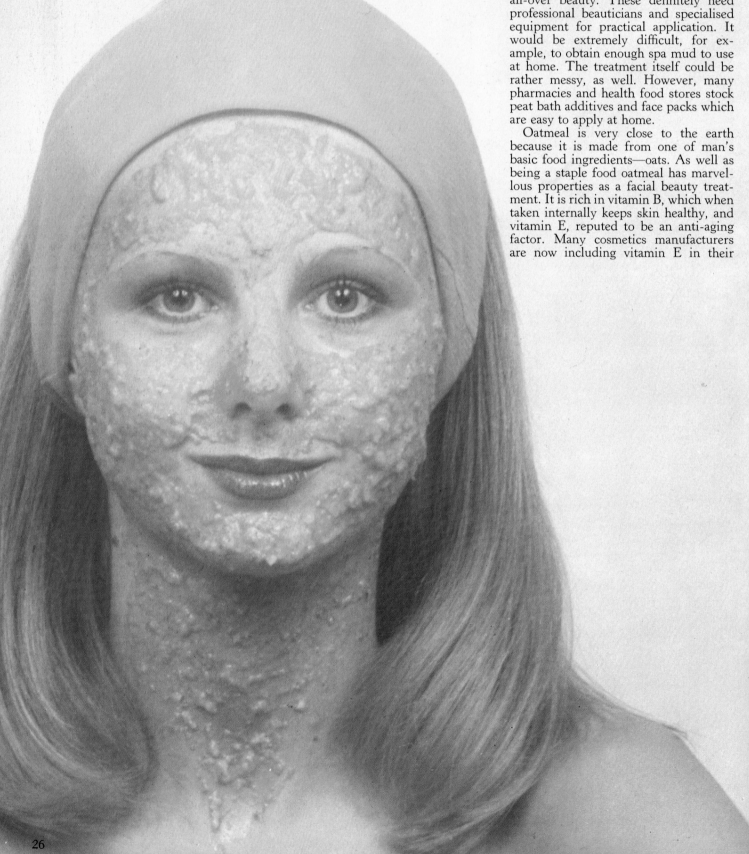

products as there is some evidence that this can also slow the aging process of the skin when applied externally. An oatmeal mask supplies more vitamin E than any other face cream so it is well worth trying.

This anti-aging mask to aid blotchy, wrinkled skin should be applied every other day. Mix two tablespoons of oatmeal with a half a cup of milk and cook gently until soft. Stir in two tea-spoons of elder flower water, avocado oil or orange water, and beat together. Allow to cool slightly, then spread over face and neck. Leave on for about 25 minutes, then rinse away with luke-warm water and blot dry.

A rejuvenating bath can be made by adding to your bath water a cup of fine oatmeal flour or a mixture of oatmeal flower and powdered orris root. These baths may prove too messy so, as an alternative, you could put the oatmeal inside a small cotton bag and rub it directly on the skin as you bathe.

Wheatgerm is another good source of vitamin E. It can be made into an excellent mask when blended with egg yolk and thinned down with a little milk. This is particularly good for dry, aging, or wrinkled complexions. It is very soothing and can be safely used every day. The mask is yellowish in colour and does not harden so lie down for a while when you apply it as the nourishing ingredients may otherwise run off the skin. Leave it on for about 20 minutes and then wash off very carefully with warm water.

Brewer's yeast is one of the richest sources of the B group of vitamins, amino acids and essential minerals. Taken internally it helps protect the skin from inflammations such as dermatitis and eczema and helps maintain brisk blood circulation. Applied externally, brewer's yeast also nourishes and stimulates the pores. To make an envigorating mask which will give you the same feeling as a brisk walk in the fresh air—glowing cheeks and lively skin-tone—mix one part of brewer's yeast powder with two parts of warm water. Pat it on firmly with fingertips, relax for 15 minutes, and then wash off with warm water. The mask

may be too stimulating for a very dry skin. If so, the invigorating process can be calmed slightly by adding some olive oil or wheat germ.

These beauty treatments may not look very good when they are on, but you will look much better as a result of using them. After a while they will take the

place of the cosmetics you may have been using to hide oily, dull or blemished skin. Face masks made from the earth are one of the most natural ways of getting, and keeping, beautiful skin. They take only a little time to prepare and, if you value a healthy complexion, are definitely worth the effort.

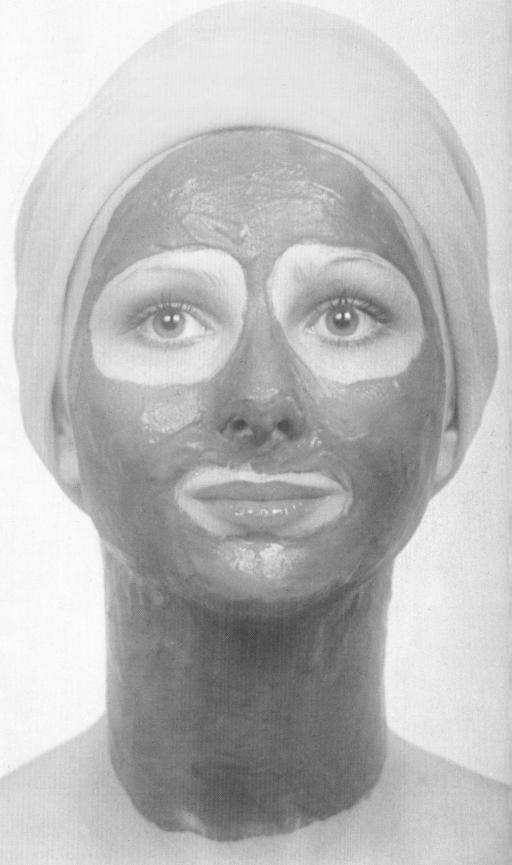

Left *Wheatgerm is an excellent source of vitamin E, which is reputed to be an anti-aging factor. When blended with egg yolk, it makes a soothing face mask that moisturizes the skin and delays wrinkling.*
Right *Brewer's yeast nourishes and stimulates the pores. It also helps to protect you from inflammations such as eczema and dermatitis, and gives you glowing cheeks and a lively skin tone.*

Highlight Your Beauty with Clever Make-up

Can you afford to ignore the way you look? Everyone can improve their looks with a little knowledge and a lot of care. Looking your best gives you inner confidence—you'll feel capable of so much more if you know you make a good first impression.

The important thing is to know how to use make-up tricks to disguise facial faults and highlight your good points—you need never be ashamed of an over-large nose or a long, thin face if they are subtly camouflaged. Hair styles, too, can do a lot to enhance your overall appearance. The right style can help to detract from your not-so-perfect features, and the length of your hair can appear to alter the proportions of your body quite drastically.

Using blushers and shapers to contour the face in such a way as to deceive the eye, needs a steady hand and a light touch. A good set of brushes will help your job enormously as the colours will not only stay on better, but will blend in more successfully, too. Buy big, floppy cosmetic brushes—they're kinder to your skin and won't leave harsh streaks of colour. Use smaller brushes for applying eye-shadow that will stay on.

The basic rule is this—use pale colours and gloss to highlight any feature that needs to draw and attract light and be brought to prominence. Pale colours also enlarge. Use darker, matte shades to give the impression of reducing and to make features appear smaller and thinner. Blend in colours thoroughly so that there are no harsh lines.

Face shapes Study the outline of your face. Is it round, square, long or oval shaped? Here's what you can do to improve the shape . . . .

Round face This will benefit from a darker powder being brushed into the sides of the face, starting from about eyebrow level, gradually fanning out into a triangle shape below the cheekbones (suck in cheeks to find the hollow) and then disappearing into nothing at the jaw-

bone. Be careful not to bring the colour round onto the chin area, as this will only have a shortening effect on a round face. Highlight chin, forehead and cheekbones to take eyes away from the sides of the face.

Hair-styles to offset a round face should have height and straight lines to help square the circle. Avoid any extra width around the cheeks, and ears area and slim off round contours with a diagonal half fringe or bangs.

Square face Emphasize your forehead and minimize your jaw to throw your face into a better balance. Play down your heavy jawline by taking your dark shader under the cheekbones and fanning colour right down over the actual jaw. Highlight just the centre spot of the chin and draw eyes upwards with the use of interesting eye make-up.

Hair styles that lend height to the face tend to offset the square jaw-line though length of hair can vary. Never let hair come level with the jaw-line, though. Soft and curvy lines, plus height, will help cut the corners, too.

Long face Make the most of your cheek-bones and minimize your jaw-line. Use a darker shade along your jaw-bone across the face and out towards temples. Highlight outermost tips of cheekbone. Finally dust your blusher along the middle of the forehead for a softening effect.

Best hairstyle for you is one with a fringe (bangs) or half fringe. Keep away from long, straight styles, though, and concentrate on those that give you width at about ear level.

Oval face You're one of the lucky ones —practically any hairstyle will suit you and you can play about with face shap-

The skilful application of modern cosmetics can do a lot to take attention away from a large nose or other facial faults.

ings too and just settle for what you like. An oval cheek colour applied just below the cheekbone will accentuate your cheek-bones, however, and if you apply a teardrop shape, it will make an oval face appear slightly rounder.

High forehead Disguise this with a soft fringe and by choosing a slightly darker-than-normal foundation to minimize the effect.

Low forehead Highlight to enlarge the area and choose a hair style which sweeps hair away from face.

Deepset, small eyes They need all the gloss, light and enlarging possible, so stick to pale coloured eye-shadows and lots of mascara.

Close set eyes Concentrate colour on outer part of eyes only. Keep the inner part of the eye and over the top of the nose pale and shiny. Pluck brows so that instead of starting immediately above the tear duct, they are slightly wider apart.

Prominent eyes For a reducing effect, cover the entire eyelid with a dark, matte eye-shadow, making it darker in the socket crease in order to make eyes seem more deeply set.

Long nose Use a darker foundation around the nostrils and just underneath the tip. A long nose can also be made to look elegantly aristocratic when it's balanced by hair massed low at the nape in a small chignon or confusion of curls.

Your hairstyle and even the length of your hair can make your face appear to be a different shape and draw attention to good points.

Wide nose Give a narrowing effect by using brown shader down each side of the nose from bridge to the nostrils and highlight the very centre of the nose to make it more prominent.

Turned-up nose To make it look straighter, put a little brown shadow on the turn of the nose to minimize the bridge crease.

Thin lips Use a brush to get a good outline and take lipstick colour slightly outside the natural lipline. Use medium and pale colours with lots of gloss to highlight.

Thick lips Using a lipbrush to give a good definite shape, take lip colour slightly inside the natural lipline. Use highlight and gloss on the inner part of the lip only.

Double chin Minimize the 'second' chin with a darker than normal foundation with a matte finish (and get busy with some facial exercises).

Receding chin Highlight your jawline with a pale shiny blusher and choose a hair style that gives you deep, fluffy curls onto the face and around and below the jaw-line.

Short neck Choose a hair style with hair above or on the same level as the ear. Long hair will only succeed in making a short neck look even shorter.

Hair styles also depend on body shape. If for instance you have short, cropped hair and you have quite a large frame, the effect may be pin-headed. Similarly a very petite person with long heavy hair may give the impression of being top-heavy—that is why a good look in a full length mirror is essential, in order for you to make the proportions right.

Attractive Eyes

Your eyes are one of the most important features you have, so make the most of them. With just a little thought and care, you can have large, sparkling eyes that will express your feelings more easily and quickly than words. Make your eyes speak for you, but first, learn how to look after them.

Your eyes can be made more healthy and beautiful if you follow a few simple guidelines to care for your eyes and keep them healthy. (And this applies as much to men as it does to women.) This attention will not only increase the health of your eyes but also your general attractiveness. Healthy, lively eyes not only highlight your face but your whole personality as well. Dull, tired and uncared-for eyes will detract from your overall attractiveness. So make a resolution to care for your eyes and guard their health.

HEALTHY EYES

To have healthy eyes is not just a matter of avoiding and treating certain things. Your eyes need everyday attention. You must actively exercise, bathe and look after your eyes frequently and consistently.

Diet Beauty really does start from the inside. What you eat is reflected in the condition of your hair, the texture of your skin and the lustre of your eyes. Keep your eyes bright and healthy by including plenty of eggs, cheese, milk, meat, fish, fresh fruit and vegetables in your diet. Vitamins A and B_2 are particularly good for eye health. You will find these in milk, cream, eggs, carrots, spinach, kidney, liver, Brewer's yeast and fish.

Sleep Regular and uninterrupted sleep is essential. It helps rest the eye muscles and on average, most people like about eight hours. If you miss out on your sleep for a lengthy period, it results in red-rimmed eyes, often bloodshot, and you'll have dark circles under the eyes. The only remedy is sleep but you can help disguise "bags" by using a pale undereye-cream in order to "lift out" shadows. The area immediately below the eye is very delicate and should never be pulled or stretched, so be very careful when applying such a cream. It's best to use a very light tapping movement in order to blend in the cream.

Eye massage Massaging the eye area helps the blood circulate and can be done at the same time as feeding the surrounding skin with a nourishing cream. The cream, or oil, will sink into the skin and plump out the skin's cells with moisture. This create's a smoother look to the skins surface and will help eliminate wrinkles and fine lines that can often be seen at the corners of eyes. Remembering that the eye area is extremely delicate, only use the soft part of fingertips to massage. Start by running the third fingertip from your nose, under the browbone and in a circle round and underneath the eye, and back to the nose. Repeat this movement, using small, circular, rotating actions keeping them light and gentle.

Eye exercises Keep your eyes relaxed by rolling them around the socket. Start by looking straight ahead, roll upwards and then on round to the outer corner of the eye. Now look down and towards the nose and finally up again. Another relaxing exercise is to first look at an object very close to you and then to look into the far distance. Blinking the lids is not an exercise, but a reflex action that happens about once every two minutes. It's designed to distribute the fluid over the eyeballs and to wash them.

CARE FOR YOUR EYES

About 80 per cent of our daily efficiency is due to our eyes. When you consider how much we depend on good sight in order to cope with everyday activities, it is amazing how careless we are with such a valuable asset. Industry alone averages a numerous amount of eye accidents a day. But carelessness about the eyes is not confined to industry. In everyday life, the eyes can be abused in many small and unnoticeable ways. The following guidelines will enable you to care for your eyes effectively.

Dirt in your eye Dust, grit, small flies, splintered wood or metal getting into your eye is the most common eye problem. The pain caused by a small particle means that you try to remove the offender immediately. And this, plus the fact that the eye will water in an attempt to wash away the particle, is the body's own way of protecting the eye. Use a wisp of clean cotton wool or the corner of a clean handkerchief to remove the particle from the eye. If, however, the particle is wedged under the upper eyelid, pull the lid outwards and downwards. Usually the particle is then carried out onto the lower lashes. If the particle is firmly stuck to the eye surface, don't rub the eye or try to remove it yourself. See a doctor quickly. If you don't, a small scratch can lead to inflammation or keratitis, inflammation of the cornea.

Lighting The eye automatically adjusts to different lighting as part of its natural function, but like everything else, it benefits from a little help. Don't read or write in a poor light, or bright sunlight, either, as this can cause dazzle and glare. Artificial lighting should be directed from behind and glancing down over the left shoulder (or right, if you are left-handed). It should not shine straight into your eyes. If a centre light is not sufficient, try adding a couple of lamps to the room. Remember, the size of the lamps required depends on the size of the room and the colour scheme. Light coloured walls reflect light and dark walls absorb light. Staircases, in particular, should be well lit, especially if they are used by an elderly person who will need extra light to compensate for deteriorating vision.

Sunlight can cause eyestress, making you tired, nervous and with a headache. So help the eyes by wearing a really good pair of polarized sun glasses. These will reduce glare reflected from flat surfaces such as sand, water and glossy magazine pages. Good sunglasses should filter out all but from about 19 to 30 per cent of the sunlight. Never stare directly at the sun because the ultraviolet rays can burn the cornea of the eye.

Eyestrain This can be caused by bad lighting, too much close work, fatigue, a fuggy atmosphere, sunbathing, motoring and reading. In a day of reading, the eye muscles may contract and relax about 100,000 times, so it's easy to see why they become tired. Television, too, can cause strain. Watching an ill-adjusted set or viewing in the dark can be harmful to the eyes. Avoid too much contrast by having enough general lighting to enable you to see things in the room easily. But don't let the light reflect into your eyes off the television screen. Never sit closer than 10 feet away from the screen and watch at eye level, glancing away frequently, to avoid strain from staring fixedly at the picture. Eyestrain from all these causes will generally clear up after a good night's rest. An eye bath with a good lotion can soothe tired eyes and relieve irritation. But unsuspected defective sight, ill-health and emotional stress can also cause eyestrain, so visit the doctor or optician if it doesn't clear quickly.

Eye tests Don't wait for blurred vision, watery eyes or headaches before getting your eyes tested. Receive checkups at regular intervals to ensure your sight has not deteriorated in any way. Children, in particular, need special attention and a careful watch kept for squinting or excessive watering. A child holding school work too close to the eyes can reveal an eye deficiency at its early stages. When the child is about eight years old, the eyes achieve adult size, but have not then developed their full stability and strength. Therefore, a child's eyes should not be exposed to the same strain as those of an adult.

Bloodshot eyes These can be the result of a cold or inflammation, and they need as much rest as possible. Use an eye mask and eye drops or an eye bath, whichever is easiest, to help soothe this condition. If eyes are not only red, but itch and are giving off a sticky discharge, then you're probably suffering from inflammation of the membrane of the eyelids and eyeball, or *conjunctivitis*. This can be caused by a smokey atmosphere, too bright a light, dust, colds, injury, or infection. An irritating substance, such as mascara or eye shadow, can also bring about conjunctivitis, so obviously, no eye makeup

should be worn whilst the problem clears itself, and afterwards, change your eye makeup to a pure, umperfumed, hypo-allergic makeup that is especially made for sensitive eyes. If there is no improvement after a few days, see your doctor.

Hygiene Avoid spreading an eye infection by being careful never to share towels. Don't rub eyes with a grubby handkerchief or dirty fingers and use cotton wool, or balls, and tissues for bathing and drying and eye infection.

Puffy eyes Puffy eyes and bags under the eyes are caused by an accumulation of excess fluid. Soak eyes with a solution of water and witch hazel (available from most chemists) and try a cooling eyemask. Start the day with a glass of warm water and a slice of lemon. This helps to flush the kidneys and disperses excess fluid.

BEAUTIFUL EYES
Makeup is used to enhance the qualities of the eyes. However, it should be applied knowledgeably and carefully. Your eyes are yours and need an individual style of makeup. Learn how to look after your eyes—and make them more beautiful.

Eye lashes They exist primarily to protect the eyes, but throughout the ages they have been used to enhance the eyes. Since they form a natural fringe all around the eye, they make it appear bigger and draw attention to the eye. Fair-haired people miss out here, so many have their eyelashes dyed for a small fee, in a beauty salon. The effect lasts for about six weeks. Mascara is excellent when used for a short period as it not only darkens the lashes, but thickens them, too. Apply one coat of mascara, first looking down and brushing top lashes from the roots, downwards, then looking up and brushing the lashes upwards. Then brush colour on to the lower lashes. Wait a minute for it to dry, then apply a second coat of mascara. Finally brush lashes through with a clean, dry brush, which should separate all the lashes. There are several types of mascara to choose from.

Wand mascaras are very convenient to use and generally come in a variety of colours apart from the normal black and brown. They are usually oil-based and

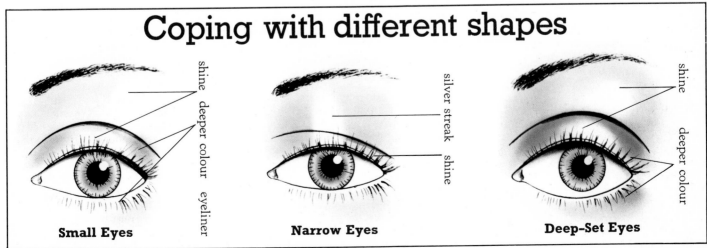

Coping with different shapes

Small Eyes — shine, deeper colour, eyeliner

Narrow Eyes — silver streak, shine

Deep-Set Eyes — shine, deeper colour

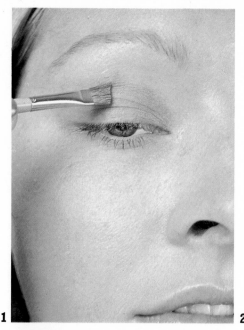

1

2

3

7

8

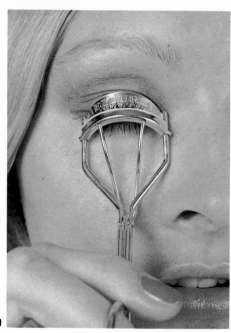

9

may smudge after the first hour. Block mascaras are water based and good for getting a strong, fast-drying layer of colour. Lash-lengthening mascara is effective when applied carefully. Recharge the brush several times to pick up the tiny fibres. When removing mascara, it's best to prevent the colour from going on to the delicate area below the bottom lashes. Do this by holding a tissue under the bottom lashes and using a cotton wool bud that has been dipped in eye makeup remover, close your eye and roll the cotton bud over the lashes, taking the mascara down the tissue. Continue this action until all the mascara has gone. To prevent lashes from drying out, smear a little vaseline on to the roots, at night.

If your eyelashes are not naturally curly, try using eyelash curlers. They are particularly effective after you have mascaraed your lashes—but only squeeze lashes very gently and be very careful to keep your hand steady.

Making the most of Your Eyes

Eye make up takes little time but makes a great difference to your looks. Follow this simple, step-by-step guide and you will get the best results. The main article advises you on the colour and texture of cosmetic to use on your eyes.
1. Use a brush to shape and blend in your eyeshadow. The colour is deepest around the socket, fading below the brow line.
2. Use a gloss to highlight the eye on the brow line.
3. Keep the eyeliner subtle with a thin line close to the eyelash roots.
4. Soften the liquid eye line with a soft-leaded eyeliner pencil.
5. Apply mascara, looking down.

6. Apply more mascara, looking up.
7. Then mascara the bottom eyelashes.
8. Brush your eyelashes through with a clean, dry brush.
9. Give your eyelashes an extra curl using eyelash curlers. Squeeze gently.
10. Check the line of your eyebrows with the pencil test. First hold the pencil against the side of the nostrils then angle the pencil from the nostril to the outer eye corner.
11. Pluck your eyebrows in the direction of hair growth.
12. Use soft, feathery strokes with an eyebrow pencil to fill in sparse eyebrows.

Eyebrows In order to make the most of the eye area, eyebrows should be kept fairly thin, neat and well-shaped. Pluck a few hairs each day and they will then keep tidy. Check where your eyebrows should end by placing a pencil at the side of the nose and swinging it across the brows in an arc in line with the outer corner of the eye. Where the pencil crosses the brow is where the brow should end. When plucking brows, spread a little cream on the brow area. Keep the skin area held taut between the second and third fingers of the left hand and using your right hand (assuming that you are right-handed) pluck out stray hairs one by one, in the direction of growth, with tweezers. Use a sharp, upward movement, and pluck from underneath only, unless you intend to alter the shape of your brows drastically. After plucking, pat skin with a pad of cotton wool that has been wrung out in ice cold water. If you need to add colour to your brows, do

it subtly with light, feathery strokes, not a hard, continuous line. Use either a very soft eyebrow pencil or a soft brown eyeshadow brush.

Eye colours Eye colour is decided by the variable amount of pigment and distributed throughout the eye's iris. Blue eyes have little pigmentation whilst brown and black eyes have a lot. Varying amounts and distribution of pigment—and not its colour—produce hazel, grey or green eyes.

The eye shadow you choose should flatter and enhance your own eye colour. Although there are no hard and fast rules, and it is best to find out by experimenting with colours, weaker eye colours such as blues, greys and hazels look prettiest with soft, pastel shades, as strong colours tend to overshadow the eyes. Similarly, bright blue, green or brown eyes can take a more definite colour, but it is very much a personal choice. Whatever colour you decide on, it should be well blended

in so that there are no harsh lines. Aim for a natural look. Invest in some brushes that will help you shape the shadows correctly or use the sponge-tipped applicators that are available. It is far more economical than using your finger—you'll find that half the shadow is still left on your finger, rather than your eyelid.

There is a large choice of eyeshadows. Creams are oil or wax based and aren't much use for greasy eyelids, as the colour just collects in creases, but they are very good for dry or crepey lids. Stick eye makeup is a much firmer form of cream and looks a bit like lipstick. It can sometimes dry out rather quickly, though. Gels are very good for greasy skins and give a longlasting stained effect, that is subtle and translucent. Liquid eyeshadows are very long-lasting, although sometimes difficult to get an even flow of colour, without the end result looking patchy. Powders are probably the easiest

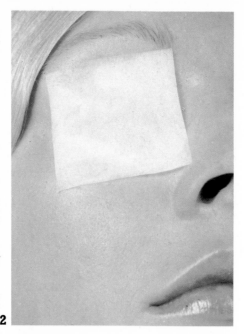

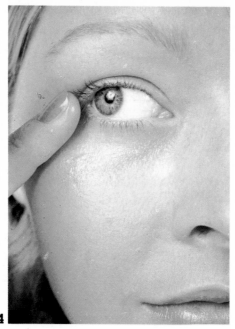

shadows to use and control although they are not always long-lasting. Often available in pearly or matt textures, many of these powder shadows can also be applied with a wet brush. This normally results in a deeper colour effect and ensures longer staying qualities.

Eye shadow is generally applied all over the lid, with the colour deepening in the socket line and fading out to a very pale colour below the brow line, though it is quite natural to use several colours and textures together. A powder shadow is often used all over the eyelid blending into a toning, paler gloss on the browbone. This helps to highlight the eye.

Eye liners outline the eye and are particularly attractive when used in a deeper, toning colour to match the eye shadow. Keep the line immediately above the roots of the eye lashes and draw it very thinly. If you use a liquid liner, soften the effect with a soft-leaded pencil liner. Make sure that the lead is soft enough by testing it on the back of your hand. If it doesn't mark easily, don't use it, as it will only drag the skin.

Optical illusions With some skilful shaping and shading the eye can be made to look completely different. Improve your eyeshape by experimenting with colour and texture.

Small eyes Pluck your eyebrows fine and light to give maximum eye area. Then cover the browbone with a pale, shiny shadow and a little on the eyelid to attract light to the eyes. Use a deeper colour shadow in the socket and faintly underneath the eyes. winging the colour out to the sides. Mascara both upper and lower lashes, using two coats on the outer lashes only. Use a thin line of eyeliner on the outer half of the eye only.

Narrow eyes Use a medium coloured eyeshadow all over the eyelid, fading up into the browbone. Then widen the eye by adding a thin streak of either silver or gold shadow to the centre of the eyelid, going from the lid straight up towards the brows. Soften the edges with a thin, dry brush.

Deep set eyes Apply a pale, shiny shadow all over the eye area from lashes to browbone. Then use a deeper blending colour close to the lash and underneath the eye.

One eye smaller than the other Extend the brow arch over the small eye, a little further out than the high point over the larger eye, using soft feathery strokes with an eyebrow pencil. Pluck a little more from under the brow of the smaller eye to make the brow slightly higher.

Straight eyebrows Pluck top of brow at both ends and angling up at the high part of the arch. Then tweeze underneath the brow to form a curve.

High, thick brows Tweezer hairs from the top of the brow allowing for the arch.

Close-together brows Pluck hairs growing over the bridge of the nose. The brow should begin approximately over the tear duct.

Arched eyebrows Pluck the top of the brow to level off the arch.

Eye Care

These guidelines will help you care for your eyes in the best possible way.

1. Soothe your eyes with a refreshing eye bath. You can buy an eye cup and eye lotion at most chemists or drug stores.
2. Relax your eyes with ice-cold pads soaked in eye lotion and put your feet up for about 10 minutes.
3. Add a sparkle to your eyes with eye drops.
4. Keep wrinkles at bay by massaging around the eye with a nourishing oil or cream. Use your fingertips to do this.
5. Roll your eyes around as a relaxing exercise.

What is in make-up?

To many people, the ingredients of the make-up they use are a total mystery. A knowledge of what goes into cosmetics will help you to choose both the most suitable and the most economical products. It has been calculated that if you apply cosmetics to your face once a day, every day, between the ages of 15 and 75, you will make nearly 22,000 applications, or 'repeated insults' as dermatologists prefer to call it. This does not count the occasional 'touching up', or a skin care routine.

The question that needs to be asked is whether make-up harms your skin. Generally speaking, the answer is, no. Apart from being good for morale, in that it makes you look so much better, make-up provides a good protective layer. It guards against dirt penetrating your pores and the weather getting the worst of your skin.

Surprisingly enough, the majority of ingredients found in today's cosmetics were present in the early 1950s. There have been one or two new materials, better refinements, closer quality control and more advanced production tech-

nology. But progress in the cosmetic industry has been slow by comparison with most others. The reason for this is that it is both difficult and dangerous for manufacturers to predict that any given product will not cause an allergic response. The responsibility is too great to take shortcuts.

When you read about astonishing new breakthroughs, remember that most trained dermatologists are sceptical. They believe that miracles are few. The beauty business relies for its living on a strong element of fashion, fantasy and dreams. Cosmetics are a psychological tranquillizer. They do make you feel more relaxed and confident in social situations.

Make-up and creams, however, do fulfil a valuable purpose in a woman's life. They help treat sub-clinical skin conditions which doctors are often far too busy to bother about. Creams protect the skin, and make it look better. Skin starts to age from the day you leave the womb. You cannot put back the clock, but you can slow it down. Many skin experts are convinced that a woman who looks after her skin is going to keep a good com-

plexion longer than a woman who does not. Make-up may be the icing on the cake, but it does form a protective layer.

Because of the strict rules governing the ingredients and pigments which go into cosmetics, it is fairly safe to assume that any one product will do your skin no harm, unless you happen to be allergic to it. You will understand that a manufacturer can produce 100,000 pots of cream, and be perfectly sure that the contents are exactly the same, but he cannot control the skin reactions of all his 100,000 customers. Some skins will react against a particular product, while other skins will be perfectly all right.

Some skins are far more sensitive to strong sun than others. Like fingerprints, all skins are different. Any product, however well tested, will prove unsuitable for some people. The scale of testing is impressive, but even in the hypo-allergenic ranges, in which all well known irritants are screened out, there is the isolated complaint from a woman with an allergic reaction.

How do you know that a particular reaction is an allergy? This is a difficult question. It is important to distinguish between a material that produces an adverse reaction in you, and one that is commonly regarded as an irritant. If you react immediately, then it is a primary irritant. The reaction occurs in the place exposed to the irritation such as the rash that appears when you spill a strong chemical on your hands.

You will not necessarily discover a true allergy the first time you use a particular product, for often it builds up slowly. The body produces anti-bodies and a rash will appear with time. Once you know about your allergy, it may prove an expensive business as you will have to stop using a cream or foundation before it is half finished. Do not attempt to use the cream again. It is not worth irritating your skin or spoiling your appearance.

If you have sensitive skin, you can play safe by only using make-up from one of the hypo-allergenic ranges available. In the end, however, it is a case of trial and error. Allergy is a complex problem. You can be allergic to almost anything such as cats, dogs, fur, household dust, strawberries and shellfish as well as pollen and lanolin. As far as make-up is concerned, chemists have discovered that it is perfume, preservatives, pigments and bacteriocides that are the sensitizers. But there are certainly many more.

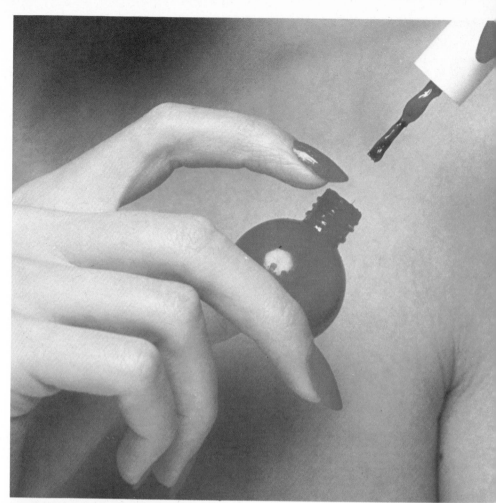

Many potential irritants are not essential to the primary use of a given product. They are included for the sake of texture and feel, or 'cosmetic elegance'. One manufacturer listed 60 known allergens removed from his cosmetic range. These included natural perfume oils, orris root, cocoa butter, arrow root, rice starch and crude lanolin.

Allergies to food are fairly general in their effects. The cosmetic allergies, however, are usually confined to a local irritation, blistering or swelling. Nail varnish is a common cause of contact dermititis. Particles are introduced to your facial skin by rubbing or scratching.

Very often, skin will accept a particular cosmetic for a number of years and then build up a reaction against it. The reason for this could be that your skin has become more sensitive because of harsh weather, central heating, too vigorous scrubbing, or even because of prescribed drugs. There is only one thing you can do, stop using the particular cosmetic and try something else.

Are natural ingredients better? Not necessarily. It is certainly absurd to say that everything synthetic is bad while all things natural are good. The current trend towards the use of natural ingredients is part of the modern spiritual urge to return to nature. It is a reaction against over-mechanization and the dehumanizing aspects of contemporary society. It is also a very clever marketing strategy with a direct appeal to people's emotions. In fact, synthetic materials are often purer than natural ones because of the controlled conditions of manufacture. Urea, for example, is often used in skin

care preparations. It can be produced either from natural gas, or by extracting it from urine. The end result is exactly the same with the same molecular structure and the same substance.

If manufacturers had to rely completely on natural material they could never cope with the high demand for cosmetics. The supply of natural materials is at the mercy of the weather. They use up an uneconomical amount of labour resources because of the preparation required. Another point to bear in mind is that if manufacturers were to use only natural materials, the resources of nature would soon be exhausted.

Cleansers

Why use cleansers? After all, soap cleanses the skin. Soap is not as effective, however, as a cream cleanser for removing make-up. This is because the oil in a cream cleanser dissolves the greasy components present in make-up. It also contains an emulsifying agent which makes the grease easier to remove.

Cleansers usually contain liquid paraffin—white oil or mineral oil—as a chief ingredient. This is specially refined for make-up and is not as thick as that used in medicines.

The emulsifier used in most make-up is glycerol mono-stearate. This is a 'surface active' soap-like substance similar to detergent. Extract of egg yolk is sometimes used as an emulsifier.

There are between eight and ten ingredients in an average cleansing cream. These are basically the same whatever the name on the jar might be. All cleansing creams contain preservatives because any cream can lie on a shelf for many months before being sold and can then be in use for several months. While in use, it is contaminated by air and fingers.

Cleansing creams usually contain some emollient oil, some colouring and perfume and water. Some cleansers, however, do not contain water. The oilier the cream, the more effective it will be in removing heavy make-up. This is why theatrical cleansers are usually thick and oily. Those cleansers that contain a lot of water are referred to as 'milks', and are an oil in water emulsion. Milks are particularly suitable for quick cleansing.

If you have a greasy skin, use a non-greasy make-up that contains mostly water, pigments and an emulsifying agent. A watery cleansing milk is best for removing such make-up. For normal skins, a cleansing milk should be used for a quick clean-up during the day. A cream cleanser can be used last thing at night for a more penetrating and efficient job.

Manufacturers claim that cleansers are more thorough cleaning agents than soap as well as less drying. Even if you do not wear make-up, diesel fumes, dirt and air pollution will do their worst by leaving a layer of oily dirt on the surface of your skin.

The last traces of cream and dirt should be removed with a skin tonic—

freshener or astringent lotion—on absorbent cotton. Tonics are usually solutions of alcohol diluted with water. Some perfume is added, as well as a little oil to help dry skins. Extract of witch hazel and rosewater is equally effective, you could make your own skin tonic with glyceroboric compound, rosewater concentrate, menthol, antiseptic, distilled water. If you have a sensitive skin, avoid alcohol based tonics. Lotions intended for greasy skins may contain astringent salts.

Moisturizers

Moisturizers have been in use for many years. It is only recently, however, that it has been suggested that they be used all the time, night and day. Skin needs water. The flexibility of the outer skin layer depends on it, and you will keep your skin looking smooth and supple by ensuring that it is moist.

The natural oil or sebum and water of your skin together form an emulsion which protects and lubricates. It prevents excessive water loss, and helps preserve the acid balance. It is true, however, that few skins, if any, have a perfect balance. The regenerative processes diminish as the skin gets older, and the body produces less of the sex hormone oestrogen. The functioning of the sebaceous glands slows down and the ability of the skin to hold water is reduced.

It is possible for the skin to age beyond its years. Premature aging is caused by external factors. Sunlight is acknowledged to be the biggest culprit in damaging skin. It destroys some of the chemical bonds in the skin and, because of increased water loss, causes wrinkling and loss of elasticity.

Holidays are times when your skin needs constant care. When sunbathing, your skin loses moisture through perspiration and if you swim, more moisture is lost into the salt water. In dry climates water evaporates rapidly off the skin's surface. Strong sun and salt water also remove the surface layer of oil.

Moisturizers have two functions: to form a waterproof barrier to keep in the moisture and to supply extra moisture. Putting water back into the skin can only be a very temporary measure. It will probably last only about an hour. The skin loses moisture very quickly. Because of this, the main use of moisturizers lies in protection. To be efficient, a moisturizer needs to be reapplied frequently and should also be worn under make-up.

Moisturizers contain less emulsifying agents than cleansers. They also contain humectants to assist in the retention of water. A common humectant is synthetic or natural glycerine.

Glycerol not only retains water, but absorbs it. It is produced by boiling vegetable or animal fats such as tallow and lard. This is done to separate the glycerol from the fatty acids. The process is called 'splitting fats'. Scientific methods can achieve the same result in a laboratory using purely synthetic materials.

Lanolin is also sometimes used as a water retainer.

Mineral or emollient oils such as wheat germ, avocado, sesame, and almond can be added. For greasier moisturizers, white petroleum jelly is sometimes used. As with cleansers, there are between eight and ten ingredients in the average moisturizer, including colour, perfume and preservatives.

Lanolin is the oil from sheep's wool. It comes in various forms, and is a staple ingredient of cosmetics. Lanolin can be refined with new scientific techniques and its chemical composition can be changed. However, there is still a question mark as to the effectiveness of the purification process in removing sheep dip. Some experts think that this is a cause of skin irritation.

Hand Creams

Hand creams are for protection and treatment and may contain Allantoin. This is a crystallizable substance obtained from allantoic fluid. It also contains foetal urine. Allantoin can be prepared synthetically by the oxidation of uric acid.

Hand cream will probably contain glycerine for moisturizing and softening, and a fine silicone oil to protect the hands with a thin, non-greasy film.

Night Creams

Night creams are greasy and heavy. They act as a lubricant and also help to retain water. Manufacturers used to call night creams 'nourishing' but this is a misleading word when applied to cosmetics.

Any cream's ability to regenerate the skin from the outside is very limited. Like other organs of the body, the lower

layers of the skin get nourishment from the blood supply. The skin is nourished both by the blood and by a well-balanced diet. No amount of cream can build new cells into your skin.

The more expensive the cosmetic, the more dramatic the advertising claims seem to be. But what evidence is there to show that vitamins, avocados, queen bee jelly, or herbs work? So called 'deep acting' revitalizing treatment creams may contain cellular tissue extracts, centella Floridana extract—obtained from a plant found only in Madagascar—honey and sometimes milk.

In most cases a moisturizer is just as effective. The latest thinking is that older skins do not need to use heavier creams. Ask yourself how many products you really need. Some women feel more confident using a cream with extravagant claims or exotic ingredients. That is why such products sell so well.

Hormones

Hormones do influence the condition of your skin and its ability to retain water. There has been a lot of controversy about them, however, and many countries ban their use in cosmetics. What worries these countries is whether the amount of hormones necessary to benefit the skin is also enough to give side effects. It is certainly doubtful that the small amount allowed in creams, because of the safety regulations, will be of any benefit at all.

Medicated products

Medicated products are aimed at skins with blemishes caused by excess oil and contain antiseptics and bacteriocides. Hexachlorophane has had a lot of adverse publicity and substitutes have already been found. Medicated creams may contain Allantoin. Many of the products in this category will be de-greasers and cleansers, sometimes with alcohol or a peeling agent to loosen the horny cells of the top layer of skin. This aids penetration and stops the pores becoming clogged by dirt and dead cells.

Lipstick

Probably the most widely used cosmetic of all is lipstick. You may think it is also one of the simplest but it can contain anything up to twenty ingredients. Basically, these are colouring and oils dispersed in a wax base. The mixture sets like crayon. Refined beeswax is still used and castor oil is a popular emollient ingredient. To make one subtle shade six or seven colours are blended together. Each colour is counted as one ingredient. There may also be vitamin oil and a sun filter to give additional protection against chapping in cold weather and strong light.

Foundations

Foundations usually contain emulsifiers, emollients and powder pigments. Transparent foundations may be based on gels produced with synthetic gelling agents.

Foundations for dry skins are based on creams with moisturizers. Those intended for greasy skin will contain an emulsifying agent with pigment and water.

It is best to use a moisturizer under make-up. One more myth that dermatologists have exploded is that make-up clogs the pores and therefore should not be used on spotty skins. Many experts believe that depression makes acne much worse and that make-up raises morale.

Powder

Face powder is a very simple product made from talc. The best come from Italian quarries. A new mine has been discovered in Queensland, Australia. It is basically a micropulverized powder very similar in texture to French chalk. Titanium oxide is sometimes added to give opacity. The only other ingredients are colour pigments and sometimes antiseptics. Treated silk is occasionally used to give added adhesive qualities.

Eye make-up

Mascara is available in two forms, as a block and in a roll-on container. The block type is a surface active material. It is similar in consistency to soap. It contains waxes and pigments. Roll-on mascara is a dispersion of pigments in a jelly-like base. It contains volatile spirit which evaporates to facilitate quick drying. Roll-on mascara may contain polymer.

Eyeshadows are sticks, similar to lipsticks. They are cast into a stick strong enough to apply without cracking and soft enough not to drag the skin. Colours and oils are dispersed in a waxy base. Cream shadows have more emollient.

Eye make-up removers contain a cleansing element such as 'tension active amphotere', perhaps Allantoin, preservatives, rosewater concentrate and distilled water. Eye-care creams are fairly simple. The consistency is light for easy and comfortable application.

Nail polish

Nail polish contains cellulose nitrate. This is a hard transparent lacquer which is used on artificial leather as well as wood and furniture. It also contains solvents. The familiar smell of pear drops is the acetates contained in the solvents. Pigment is used to give the desired colour. Polish remover is a mixture of acetone and esters. A little oil is added to retard the drying time of nail polish.

Finally, taking cosmetics generally, those that are animal based may offend some conservationists and vegetarians. The part that comes from animals is likely to be glycerol. Glycerol can also be synthetically produced. Any reputable manufacturer will give a list of preparations which are not animal based. on request.

Knowing what is in the cosmetics you use will save you wasting money on products which claim to do more than they can. It should also convince you that make-up is not always bad for the skin.

Make the Most of Your Hair

Good-looking hair is essentially healthy, shiny and clean. Treat it like an expensive fabric because it needs just as much care and attention to prevent it from deteriorating.

When hair first sees the light of day, it is just about perfect. The troubles begin soon after as we grow older. Brushing, perming, colouring and even washing can damage hair. So, too, does direct heat whether from a hot hair dryer or brilliant sunshine. When hair is processed by chemicals or damaged in other ways, it tends to lose vital elasticity, becomes brittle and splits.

How can you give hair the care it needs to survive? First you should know what hair is and how it grows. The more you know, the more sense hair care will make.

What is hair for?

Its original function was to keep animals warm and afford protection. Today, hair tends to be associated with the appearance we present to the world. Hair is the most dramatic and convenient erotic signal available to both men and women. For a woman, beautiful hair is one of the most powerful weapons in her sexual armory. For a man, it is the outward, visible sign of his virility.

What is hair?

Hair is a thread-like horny substance, made of keratin, a protein which is also responsible for the hardness of nails. The hair you see is "dead", the living hair is at the roots. Here, hair grows out of a pocket or pit in the scalp called a follicle at the base of which is a tiny stud: the papilla, where growth begins. Next to each follicle is a sebaceous gland which produces the hair's natural oil.

Hair can be coarse, medium or fine, depending on the diameter of individual hair fibres. Most hair is a mixture of textures with a bias to one type. Whether hair is curly or straight will depend on the shape of the hair follicle; straight hair comes from round follicles, curly hair comes from oval-shaped follicles.

How fast does hair grow?

Hair grows about half an inch a month and most rapidly between the ages of 15 and 30. Growth speeds up in the summer, and slows down in the winter. The average hair grows for about three years and then falls out. A new hair then replaces it. We lose between 50 and 80 hairs a day.

There are about 120,000 hairs on your head, but more if you are a blonde. Each hair is made up of three layers. The cuticle or outer layer has tiny, overlapping transparent scales. When these lie flat, hair appears shiny, but if the scales are lifted, hair seems rough and dull. Conditioning rinses help to keep hair soft and smooth.

The cortex or middle layer of hair contains the colouring pigment. Bleaches and colourants work by penetrating the outer scales so that colour is added or subtracted from the cortex. Perms take effect in a similar way. The inner layer or medulla may not be present in very fine hair. The porous nature of hair allows for the penetration of chemicals. It varies along the length of each hair, the youngest bit near the scalp being the least porous. Dry hair is more porous than oily hair. The agents used in bleaches, tints and perms capitalize on the porous character of hair. By making hair respond like blotting-paper the chemical agents used in these treatments are quickly absorbed and bring about changes in colour and curliness. But none of these treatments should be used on hair that is in poor condition.

Healthy hair is beautiful hair. The most expensive cut or hairdo will not make dull, lustreless, out-of-condition hair look attractive. So before you begin to think of perming, colouring or styling, think first about the healthiness of your hair. With a little more time and trouble you can learn to give your hair the care and attention to keep it glossy, shining and stunning to look at.

How often should hair be washed?

All hair needs to be washed regularly about once a week or three times a fortnight, according to the type of hair you have. A mild shampoo should be used. There is great competition in the profitable shampoo market and it is quite possible that there is one shampoo which will suit your hair better than another. However, as all shampoos are basically made of detergent, water and some fatty ingredient, you may find a cheaper shampoo does just as much for your hair as a more expensive brand. All those extra benefits such as ingredients of egg, lemon, beer or herbs don't necessarily make one shampoo any more effective than another. Try different sorts of shampoo until you find the best one for your hair.

Does oily hair need washing every day?

Experts say no. Over-washing reduces the hair's natural oils and may make the sebaceous glands work harder to produce more. If hair becomes greasy at the roots soon after washing, it is because the sebaceous glands increase the output of oils. Some trichologists feel that some of the stronger modern shampoos do not help the situation. They recommend "grass-roots" beauty aids and herbal preparations.

Does hair need brushing every day?

Yes, the 100 strokes a night bit is an old maxim which does have merit. So long as you brush your hair every day to clear it of its surface dirt you need not go as far as 100 strokes. Brushing helps to spread the natural oil down from scalp to hair ends and also smoothes down scales. Back-combing ruffles the scales and can cause damage. Always brush hair when it is dry. Brushing wet hair causes the ends to split.

The benefits of brushing are: to tone the circulation of the scalp—increased blood supply to the hair roots makes them better nourished; to relax face and neck tension; to clean the hair of daily dust and dirt.

Which is the best way to brush hair?

Hang your head down and brush away from the scalp first. Tilting your head forwards increases the blood supply to the scalp and stimulates the hairs. Brushing distributes the hair's natural oils along the hair shaft.

Which kind of brush do you need?

The best hair brushes are made of bristles which come from wild boar. The tiny scales or hooks clean the hair as they pass through it. Fine hair needs a softer brush which does not scratch the scalp. Very thick long hair needs a bigger brush with stiffer bristles. Short or curly hair needs a narrow brush with a longish rectangular head and bristles widely spaced in groups. Medium length hair requires a half-round radial brush. The latest designs are called half-radial or all-round radial which means that they have bristles half or all the way round, and they are especially useful for styling the hair.

How can you distinguish the best quality brush?

With brushes you really do get quality according to the price you pay. More often than not the less you pay the less

time a brush will last. Cheaper brushes do fill a need but try to avoid cheap nylon-filled brushes which have spiky ends. Brush ends should always be 'rondated', rounded off to stop hair splitting. Solid filament, nylon quill brushes with properly finished ends may be fine for styling but they cannot clean and beautify hair in the same way as can a bristle brush.

Remember, a good brush, if properly cared for, will last for ages. Wash it in soft, soapy, lukewarm water. Pull out coarse hairs by hand. If you have an old disused hair brush use it to remove tangled hairs. Most important: leave the brush to dry near an open window and not near direct heat. Place the brush so that the bristles hang down to enable the water to drip away from the base.

What is the best kind of comb to use?

A good comb should be hand finished with teeth that are not too sharp. Sharp teeth snag and snap hair. Use a fine comb for fine hair, an all-rake comb with wider spaced teeth for thick hair and for combing wet hair.

The best way to comb out knots is to start at the ends and work gradually upwards, bit by bit until you reach the crown.

The perfect head of hair is rare and we all seem to have one problem or another. Hair can be dry or greasy, dull and lifeless or full of dandruff, have split ends or be prone to thinning. Hair care is usually divided into treatment for specific hair problems.

Fine hair is more common in blonde and "mousey" hair. Lightweight, fragile, and "baby-fine", it is easily split and difficult to keep looking tidy. One solution is first to get it expertly cut, then to use an after-shampoo cream rinse and a bristle brush to lessen static electricity which makes it difficult to keep in place.

Curly hair, the envy of those with straight hair, has problems too. It is often unmanageable and wants to go its own way. Damp weather may make it frizz, so

do steamy bathrooms or kitchens. Straightening, which is a perm in reverse, smoothes down the waves for a time, but it is not the ideal solution. Stretching is not good for hair. Too much will lead to breaking. Far more preferable is the gentle coaxing of the modern brush-and-blow-dryer technique. Strands of hair are held taut while a stream of hot air dries it. A touch of hairspray acts as a weatherproofer to stop the damp from curling it again. Only hairsprays made with resins, rather than old-fashioned shellac, should be used.

Coarse hair is more likely to be curly than straight and tends to lack elasticity. It often looks rather dry and is harsh to the touch. Lack of elasticity makes it weak so avoid back-combing and spiky rollers and brushes. It needs to be treated with extra care. A spray-on aerosol hair dressing helps to increase the shine.

Dry hair is dry because the sebaceous glands are not producing enough oil to lubricate the hair or because hair has been dried out through processing with perms and bleaches. Dry hair looks dull and tends to have split ends. Regular brushing, which stimulates the scalp circulation helps, so do massage and regular conditioning. Olive, almond or coconut oil are good conditioners and work just as well if not better than the commercial but less messy products.

A scalp massage once a week is good for all hair and 10 minutes a day can especially benefit poor, dry hair. Sit at a table and prop yourself up on your elbows, placing your hands either side of your head, spreading out fingers. Using tips of fingers, knead the scalp in little circles, just moving the scalp and not rubbing the head.

If you have dry hair don't sit under too-hot hair dryers. Keep your head covered in hot sunshine which is very drying. Use only the mildest of shampoos. Use an after-shampoo conditioning cream rinse, too, to smooth down hair scales, prevent tangling and make hair easier to comb.

Oily hair and oily skin often go together, both caused, in teenage years, by hormonal changes. Some shampoos, said to be especially for greasy hair, may contain stronger detergent, but this is not necessarily beneficial as they may irritate the scalp and aggravate the problem. Excessively greasy hair can lead to thinning, too, because the abundant oil interferes with the normal cycle of hair growth.

What can be done to prevent split ends?

Split ends need to be cut off. It is a good idea to have hair trimmed regularly every four or five weeks, even if you are growing it. Avoid rubber bands, sharp clips, spiky brushes and combs and don't brush hair when it is wet.

What is dandruff and what can be done about it?

Dandruff is an exaggeration of the scaling process by which the skin renews

Ten Tips for Hair Care

1 Eat a well-balanced diet with plenty of protein, fresh fruit and vegetables. Cut down on fried food, starches and sweet sugary foods.
2 Wash hair regularly with a mild shampoo.
3 Have hair trimmed every four or five weeks to get rid of split ends and have it styled.
4 Choose the equipment you use for your hair with care. Use hand-finished combs, a good brush, no elastic bands but rather the covered variety. Don't use harsh nylon or metal combs

5 Don't brush hair when it is wet but use a smooth-edged, wide-toothed comb.
6 Increase circulation and the blood supply to hair roots with regular massage. Not recommended for very oily hair.
7 Remedy the effects of sunshine, pollution and other damaging agents with regular conditioning.
8 Avoid back-brushing and back-combing.
9 Never over-wash hair because this strips the hair of its natural oils.
10 Take regular exercise.

itself and can have a variety of causes: poor scalp circulation, over-harsh shampoos, too-oily scalp, even nervous tension which leads to scalp tightness so preventing the blood from bringing the proper nourishment to the hair roots. It seems to be the most common hair problem among both men and women in all social and age groups.

One cause of dandruff is attributed to the sebaceous glands producing too much oil. An ideal treatment should aim at stopping this over-production, but this does not always meet with much success. The alternative is to control the condition by removing the dandruff scales and minimizing the spread of infection with an anti-dandruff treatment shampoo. Some doctors prescribe products containing selenium sulphide, but it is not advisable to use it frequently. An ordinary shampoo should be used in between.

Excessive falling and thinning hair can be caused by illness, emotional stress or shock. Some women find their hair looks glossier during pregnancy but experience hair loss about three or four months after childbirth. Hair growth returns to normal a few months after pregnancy.

A very common problem is that of hair which becomes greasy at the scalp yet stays dry at the ends. There is no doubt, that this condition is most likely to occur with long hair. The hair at the ends has been in existence the longest and consequently has suffered more drying and damage. The answer? Have hair trimmed regularly. Prior to shampooing, soak a pad of cotton wool in witch hazel and apply to scalp along partings if roots are excessively greasy. After shampooing use a conditioner on the ends only. Use a bristle brush to distribute the oil down the shaft.

Brush lightly and regularly.

Can hair sprays be damaging?

Dull, lifeless hair may result from excessive use of a hair spray. Some may have a drying effect but most modern sprays are easy to brush out. An anti-lacquer shampoo should remove any film but for excessive coatings buy some powdered Borax from the chemist. Mix one ounce with a cream shampoo and shampoo in the usual way but keep the second application of shampoo on the hair for 10 minutes before rinsing. To remove build-up from greasy hair, soak a pad of cotton wool in surgical or methylated spirit, divide the hair and apply along partings. Shampoo after 10 minutes. This leaves the hair clean.

Although you cannot change your hair type through diet, you can ensure healthy hair by including proteins such as eggs, milk, cheese, meat and fish in your diet and less of the processed sugars and starches. All of these are better for your figure and general health, too.

Hair is a barometer of health so your insurance for next year's healthy hair begins now with the proper care, the right foods, fresh air, exercise and sleep.

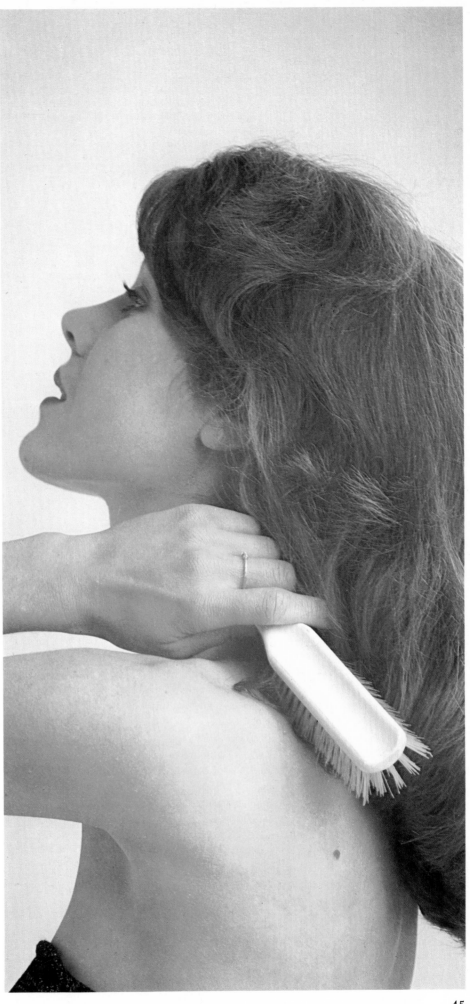

Coping With Unwanted Hair

We either have too little in the right places or too much in the wrong ones. That's the trouble with hair. But it's a very important part of our lives. Freud felt that hair demonstrates our sexuality on a subconscious level.

Having noticeable hair in places not normally associated with hair, such as the legs, arms, stomach and back can make a woman feel less feminine and causes intense misery. She might even feel a bit of a freak.

But unwanted hair is said to affect as many as one-10 women. And is it necessarily so undesirable and unattractive? Lots of men find body hair attractive. You have only to sit on any Mediterranean beach to realize that Continental girls don't bother to shave under arms like the Americans and British.

We all have downy hair on our skins, but blonde down doesn't show and dark down does. Fighting the fuzz is more of a problem to the brunette, and heredity and nationality have a lot to do with the pattern of hair growth.

You may be hairy because your mother or father was hairy. Mediterranean types with dark hair are more likely to get a growth of dark, coarse hair on the body than blonde Nordic types. It's just 'one of those things'.

Have hormones got anything to do with it? Only in a minority of cases. But there are some diseases which have superfluous hair growth as a side effect.

Hairy legs may upset one girl but not cause a shadow of worry to another. How much of a problem you have depends not only on the number and colour of the hairs, but also on your state of mind. It helps to realize that you are not unique. It's not freakish to get hair round the nipples, on the tummy, at the base of the spine, on the thighs, and so on. What you can do about it depends on the time and money you want to spend, and where you live.

Shaving: This is probably the cheapest, quickest and easiest method of home hair removal, but it's best for legs and underarms rather than arms and face because regrowth is generally quick and prickly.

This is not simply because shaving makes hair grow thicker (if that were so the baldness problem would be solved), but because the hair is cut bluntly at the skin surface and the hairs' fine points removed. And regrowth tends to be darker and therefore most obvious.

The best kind of razor for legs or underarms is one with a shaped head using single-edged blades to reduce the possibility of accidental cuts or nicks. To get a smooth finish, use plenty of foamy lather—a man's aerosol shaving foam makes the job much easier. After shaving, rinse away all the soap and dust on a little talcum powder. Don't apply an anti-perspirant under arms directly after shaving because it will sting (at the very least) and may even cause a rash.

Electric shavers? They have different blades for long and short hair and they

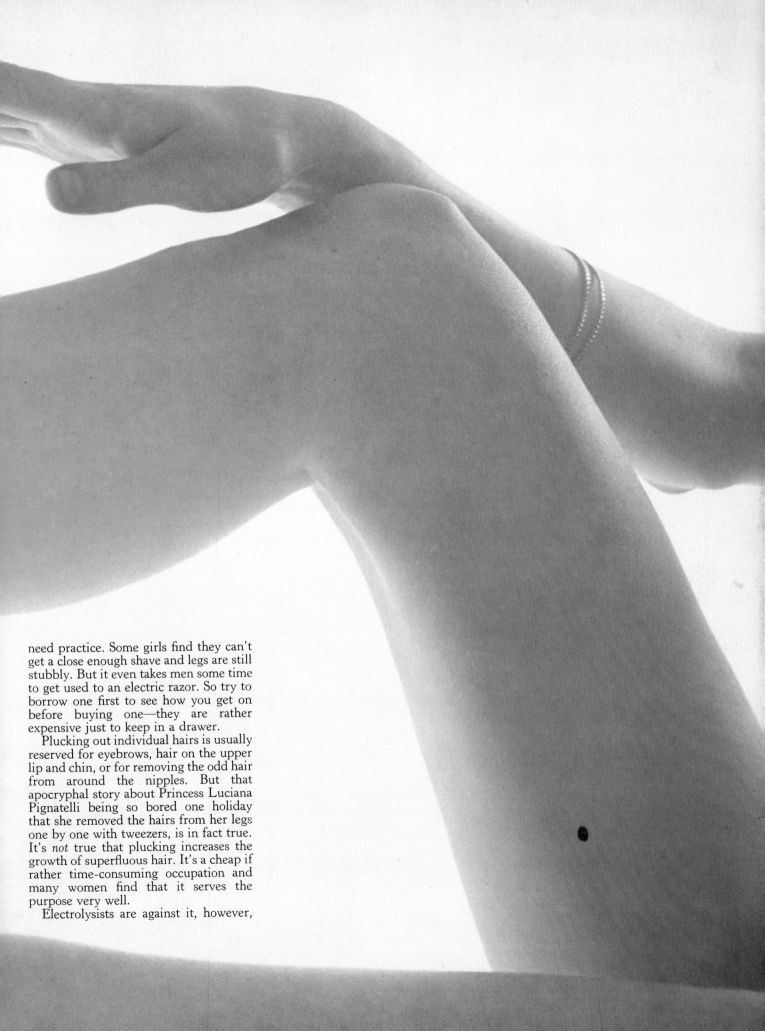

need practice. Some girls find they can't get a close enough shave and legs are still stubbly. But it even takes men some time to get used to an electric razor. So try to borrow one first to see how you get on before buying one—they are rather expensive just to keep in a drawer.

Plucking out individual hairs is usually reserved for eyebrows, hair on the upper lip and chin, or for removing the odd hair from around the nipples. But that apocryphal story about Princess Luciana Pignatelli being so bored one holiday that she removed the hairs from her legs one by one with tweezers, is in fact true. It's *not* true that plucking increases the growth of superfluous hair. It's a cheap if rather time-consuming occupation and many women find that it serves the purpose very well.

Electrolysists are against it, however,

saying that plucking stimulates the hair to grow again because every time you yank it out, blood flows in and nourishes the area. Certainly, it is easier to get quicker, better results with electrolysis on 'virgin' hair that has not been plucked, shaved or creamed away.

On the other hand, advocates of waxing (which is really wholesale plucking) say that eventually the root will give up the unequal struggle and go out of business. You can get evidence for both sides...the dark coarse chin hair which seems to grow stronger than ever no matter how many times you pluck them out; and the coarse, thick, heavy growth on your legs which grow back sparsely after waxing.

Depilatories. There's nothing new about hair removal. Ancient Egyptians used to have the fuzz whisked away with a syrup of sugar and lemon. It's an Arabian beauty idea, too, and still used today. Take half a cup of sugar, the juice of half a lemon, boil into syrup; when it is warm and pliable, (not too hot or you will burn yourself), apply to hairs. Let it set, then rip it off like a sticky plaster, hairs and all.

If that sounds a bit crude, it is at least better than the recipe from 1808 composed of ants eggs, gum of ivy, gum arabic, vinegar and orpiment (said to be one of the strongest known poisons).

But modern depilatories are considerably safer and more acceptable—they're generally wax or cream.

Cream depilatories contain a chemical to dissolve the hair just below the skin level...usually calcium thioglycollate. They are likely to cause irritation if used repeatedly on the face, so best kept for legs or arms. The first modern creams used to smell horrible but now they all seem to be rose-scented. Chemical defuzzing lasts longer than shaving, but not as long as waxing.

You shouldn't use a depilatory cream or lotion on skin that is sore or broken or if you have pimples, and if you use it frequently, it will make the skin dry. Keep depilatory creams away from the eyes or other tender parts—so don't consider it for 'bikini hair' removal. If you use the cream under arms, wait about eight hours before applying an antiperspirant or deodorant. There is no medical evidence to suggest that depilatory creams affect regrowth in any way. According to one American expert, regrowth may appear darker because the lighter coloured hair ends have been removed. As these ends are also finely tapered, regrowth may seem slightly harsher. However, as the hair grows, the fair, fine tips are said to re-form.

If the skin feels sore after using a depilatory cream, you may have a sensitive skin—try swabbing the area with a neutralizing solution of 1 part lemon juice or vinegar to 7 of cold water, immediately after the cream has been removed. Pat dry and apply a little zinc ointment.

You may be leaving the cream on too long. Remove it the moment it has done its work. Always follow instructions carefully, and rinse thoroughly with cold water. Pat dry gently—don't scrub.

Aerosol foam depilatories are the newest method of applying hair removing creams for legs. They are quicker and easier to use and the modern cans can be sprayed at any angle, even upside down. Hair is gone in four-10 minutes. It's generally more expensive but much more convenient.

Waxing is a method of hair removal often used in beauty salons where beauticians heat pans of wax, judge the right temperature (not too hot and not too hard), apply it in strips and rip it off quickly, taking the hairs with the wax. It can work out an expensive business but an ankle-to-thigh wax-away could last for weeks. A good idea for just before a holiday. You can have a 'bikini wax' round the top of the thighs, and waxing is used to remove hair from backs, stomachs, arms and face as well as legs.

Waxing removes hair from the roots and so it lasts longer than other methods, except electrolysis. Frequent waxing

---

Unwanted body hair can be a source of great misery and embarrassment — but it's easy to remove it with one of many modern methods.

---

does seem to have a discouraging effect. Hair grows back usually more finely and sparsely.

Bad points? It's tedious to do yourself at home—and a home wax kit can be quite expensive. It does hurt—just like removing a sticky bandage. But the quicker you rip the better. And judging just the right moment to apply the hot wax isn't easy.

Cold wax can be an alternative method for arms or legs. You buy a tube of sticky cold wax, apply it in strips with a spatula in the direction of hair growth, then press on strips of cotton material, which you rip off quickly. Cold wax strips are more expensive, ready prepared between two sheets of gauze. But one strip could last a number of times.

Bleaching is one way of making existing hair less conspicuous...good for down rather than thick, coarse hairs. There are various recipes for a home-bleach...two teaspoons of Fuller's Earth mixed to a paste with one teaspoon 20 vol. peroxide. Or two tablespoons 20 vol. peroxide and six drops of ammonia. Or 30 vol. peroxide mixed with two or three drops of ammonia, Fuller's Earth or soapflakes. Apply the paste. Leave on for five-10 minutes (depending on how sensitive your skin is), then rinse off with cold water. Apply the liquid bleach mixture with cotton balls. Bleach down on upper lip or on arms. Electrolysists sometimes advise bleaching in between sessions.

Electrolysis is the only permanent method of hair removal. It's usually expensive and takes longer than you think. Don't expect one session to clear all your hairs for ever. Ask for an estimate if you want some idea on how long it is going to take—some heavy growths of hair can take years to remove completely. Lighter growths, especially if you haven't plucked, creamed or waxed before, may need only five sessions. Choose your operator carefully because you can be scarred in the hands of an unskilful eletrolysist.

There are two main methods of treatment—diathermy or galvanism, but diathermy or short wave is more widely used and is quicker. With this, an electric current is passed through a fine needle into the hair follicle to kill the hair at the root. With galvanism, each hair is destroyed with an indirect current and the needle is held in place for at least 10 seconds.

Does it hurt? That depends—everybody's pain threshold varies but it is usually considered bearable. Sometimes just a stinging sensation is experienced. Small spots may appear after the treatment but with a skilled operator, you shouldn't get any permanent scarring. You can only go by reputation and recommendation. And if you aren't satisfied, don't continue with the same operator. Prices vary depending on the area, so 'shop around' before your first session.

After treatment keep the skin dry, cleanse with cream not water; don't use skin tonic; try to do without make-up for 24 hours; use calamine lotion on any spots or rash.

In between sessions, electrolysists prefer clients to cut hair with scissors—not to pluck, wax or use depilatory creams.

It's probably a good idea to have electrolysis on your face or for odd hairs on the body—legs might prove too expensive—or for the backs of your upper thighs, where it is difficult for you to reach.

Although there's a do-it-yourself 'electric pencil' on the market, it isn't advisable to use it because it takes skill to insert a needle into a hair follicle and you could cause scarring or other disfigurement.

Disguising hair on the face with cosmetics isn't successful and the ways to disguise leg hair are obviously dark, thick stockings or trousers. If you are embarrassed about hairy arms you can always wear long sleeves. But the real answer with unwanted hair is not to disguise but to remove with one of the above methods. Whichever you choose, don't worry and get a phobia about it... like the young girl who wore a thick scarf up to her eyes even in summer so she could hide the dark down on her upper lip.

Most people have it...but you don't have to if you don't want it. That's one of the comforting aspects of modern science.

The Secrets of Leg Care

Legs are a particularly hard-working part of the body. It is estimated that in a normal day the average woman walks approximately 27,000 steps—or nearly seven miles. With all that work to do, legs deserve to be near the top of the beauty- and health-care list. Yet far too often, they tend to be taken for granted and are frequently overworked and neglected. Only when they start to ache after the damage has been done, do most people wake up to the fact that their legs do require some care.

It is well worth paying attention to both the health and appearance of your legs, for they are far more than purely functional. Indeed, legs can be a great

beauty asset that can make or break a really good figure. Because legs vary in shape and size so much, there is really no such thing as the 'perfect' pair of legs. The classical long, slender leg, the sturdy, short leg, the fat leg and the thin leg can all look attractive in their own right. The important thing is that you know how to make the most of your legs and how to show them off to their best advantage.

Legs are composed of four parts—the ankle, the calf, the knee and the thigh. It is the proportions of these parts that make up the shape and size of the leg as a whole.

Ankles are the vulnerable bony joints

that connect the leg to the foot. It is basically the size and arrangement of the bones, muscles and tendons in this joint that determine the thickness of the ankle itself. There is very little that can be done to alter this structure or arrangement although exercises can help to strengthen it. Consequently, not much can be done permanently to change the shape of a thick or a thin ankle. It is possible, however, to disguise the basic size of the

ankle with a clever and subtle use of cosmetic shading. To make thick ankles look thinner, for example, try using a little powder shadow in the hollows below and behind the ankle bones.

One common problem with ankles is that they tend to swell up, especially in hot weather, or after sitting in one place for a long time or on a long flight when the reduced cabin pressure allows the body fluid to drain into the legs. This is quite natural and nothing to worry about. To minimize any discomfort it is a good idea to remove restricting nylon stockings or tights and not to wear close-fitting shoes. If, on the other hand, your ankles tend to swell up regularly for no apparent reason or appear to be swollen all the time, it is best to see your doctor as this could be an early sign of some kidney or heart trouble.

Ankles will also swell up simply because they are tired. If you have to stand on your feet all day or know that you have a long way to walk, make a point of wearing a comfortable pair of shoes, preferably with a low heel. When you get home in the evening and your feet are tired, kick off your shoes and sit with your feet up for about 15 minutes. Make sure that they are above the level of your hips, so that the excess fluid can drain out of the legs and thus relieve the pressure on the ankles and feet.

One of the most soothing cures for tired and swollen ankles and feet is to plunge them first into a bowl of hot water and then straight into a bowl of cold water and to continue alternating between these two temperatures—making sure that the ankles are fully immersed each time.

If your ankles suffer from water retention and are often puffy, dissolve a cupful of Epsom salts in a bowl of hot water and bathe your feet in this for a while. A vigorous rub with a loofah on and around the ankle will also help to reduce the swelling by stimulating the circulation and dispersing the fluid.

Moving up from the ankle is the calf, probably the most frequently exposed and scrutinized part of the whole leg. The shape and size of the calf depends upon the arrangement and development of the calf muscles. These are the muscles that are largely employed in walking, running and general leg movement. If someone has been trained as a ballet dancer or as an ice-skater or plays a lot of sport, for example, he or she will inevitably have well-developed calf muscles. There is virtually nothing that can be done to reduce the size of large muscular calves. Exercises, will, however, help to increase the size and

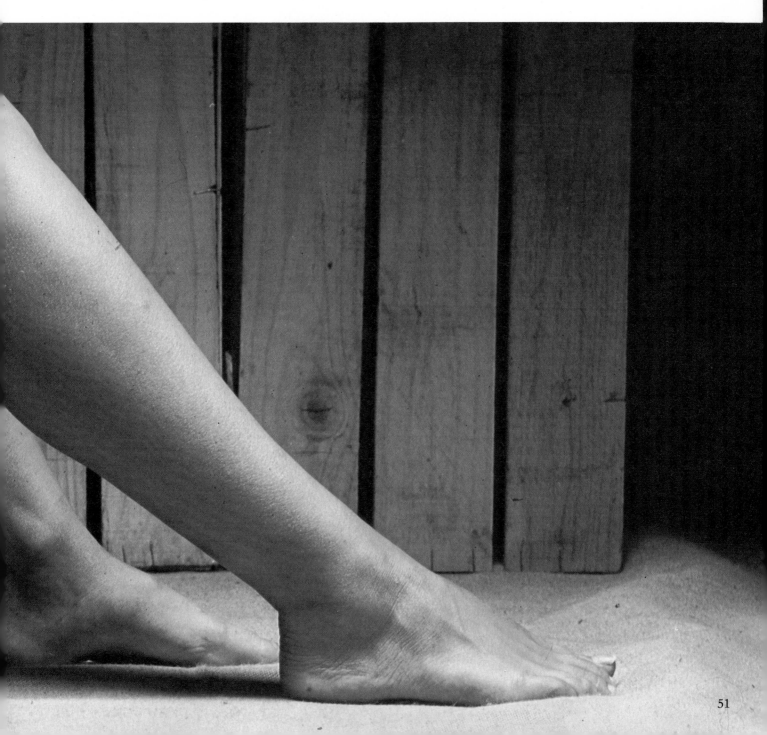

This in turn results in a swelling of the vein in that area producing a varicose vein.

Nobody has yet found out exactly what causes them. One theory is that the weakness in the valve is due to standing still for a long period of time. This drains the blood to the legs and puts extra pressure on the leg veins and valves to get the blood back to the trunk. Some people think that it is due to the lack of roughage in Western diets, noting that varicose veins are practically unheard of in more primitive societies. The lack of roughage leads to constipation which in turn causes pressure in the abdomen into which the blood flows from the legs. Secondly, constipation causes straining to empty the bowels that increases the pressure in the legs.

Prevention is far better than cure. When you feel your legs getting tired, try to relax for a few minutes. Sit down on the floor, facing a wall and then start climbing up the wall with your feet. Wriggle forward on your buttocks until your legs are straight up the wall and make a right angle to your body.

Alternatively, sit down for a few minutes and massage your legs briskly, working up the leg from the ankles. Start by kneeding the outside of the legs with both hands quite firmly, working right up to the thighs. Then start again at the ankles and move up the leg with gentle, circular movements of the hands. Finally, stroke the legs with firm, long strokes from the feet upwards, as though you were straightening and pulling up a pair of tights.

If you notice varicose veins appearing, it is a good idea to start wearing support stockings. With a regular examination of the legs at bathtime, for example, you should be able to spot them early enough to prevent them developing any further. If you are in any doubt about this or if your varicose veins become worse, you should consult your doctor.

Minor surface and spider veins should not be confused with varicose veins. These are thin, red to blue veins running across the surface of the leg which, like bruises, can easily be disguised by applying a little liquid foundation to the affected area.

Since the calves are so frequently exposed to view, especially during the summer, it is important to keep them looking their best at all times. Smooth, blemish-free calves are extremely pleasing and attractive.

Like any other part of the body, the skin on the calves tends to dry out and become scaly and flaky. A little light moisturizing cream or lotion rubbed into the legs each night with the finger tips will help to keep the skin smooth and supple.

It is also important to remove the unwanted hair on the calves regularly. Waxing is one of the best methods for removing this superfluous hair. It not only removes the hair very effectively

strength of weak or flabby calves.

You can influence the shape of the calf by the type of shoe you wear. A shoe with a heel, for example, lifts the ankle and throws the calf muscles into a slight state of tension. It is this tension that pulls the calf muscles into the classical club shape that is so elegant and much admired.

Cramps in the calves can be very troublesome—particularly at night. Basically they occur when there is a sudden, painful contraction of the calf muscles resulting from an increased irritability of the tissues which establish contact between the nerves and muscles. This is caused by a number of factors including a lack of calcium, anaemia, a poor circulation and a sudden loss of body fluids through heavy sweating or diarrhoea.

The best way to deal with cramps when they do occur is to try and stretch the affected muscle as far as possible. This will be uncomfortable but it helps to bring the muscle out of its spasm.

When the intense pain abates, massage the area gently but firmly to restore a good circulation as quickly as possible and to prevent the cramp recurring.

If you do suffer from night cramps fairly regularly, you can take a few simple steps to prevent them occurring. Warming the bed with an electric blanket or a hot water bottle before you get into it and wearing bed socks to keep your feet warm will both help to make sure that your legs do not get cold during the night.

Varicose veins are another problem that particularly affects the calves. These are the unsightly, dark blue, enlarged and knobbly veins that can often be seen threading their way across the back of the leg. These varicose veins form because the small valves in the leg veins that help to maintain the flow of blood back to the heart break down and fail to close properly. Consequently, there is a slow seepage of blood back through the valve and down the leg which creates a pooling effect around the weak valve.

but also retards re-growth, so that the treatment is only required every six weeks or so. Depilatory creams and lotions are another satisfactory way of removing hair but should be used more regularly. Always be sure to read the instructions carefully before using. Bleaching is generally less satisfactory as it tends to bleach the skin as well as the hair. Shaving works too, in so far as it removes the hair, but unfortunately the hair tends to grow back hard and bristly.

Moving on to knees, very few people would rate them as an important or attractive feature of their legs. But often attention is focussed on the knees when they coincide with the hemline of a skirt or are revealed when you sit down. Knobbly knees and plump knees are virtually impossible to change but it is possible to disguise flaws and faults. A touch of powder blusher, for example, on the sides of the knees will make them appear slimmer. If you have particularly long thighs and short calves so that your knees seem low on the leg try drawing a thin line of pale liquid foundation up the centre of the shin. Then put a rosy highlight of pink blusher high up on each knee. This helps to create the illusion of a longer calf and restores balance to the proportions of the leg.

Many people have scars on their knees, remnants of old playground accidents. The best method of hiding them is to use a liquid foundation smoothed over the scar with moist fingers or a damp sponge. Allow the liquid to dry before blending it into the leg with a pad of cotton wool.

Knock knees occur when people stand with their knees turned in together. They are not particularly elegant or attractive. This and pigeon toes can only be corrected by a conscious effort to remember to stand with the feet and knees straight and facing the front.

Heavy thighs—muscular or fat thighs —are the bane of many people's lives. Just as with muscular calves, it is very difficult to reduce the size of well-developed muscular thighs. Fat thighs, on the other hand, are easier to deal with. Contrary to popular opinion, legs do respond to a slimming diet. The only thing is that they may be the last parts of the body to show the effects of dieting, and some people lose patience before they see the benefits on their legs and abandon their diet prematurely.

Exercise can be a great help in firming up flabby thighs and reducing their size. Massage, too, can be used to break down and disperse the hard, globular deposits of cellulite that can plague upper thighs.

Years ago, when legs were covered by long skirts and layers of petticoats, they were not a problem. One Victorian woman wrote, 'There is no part of the human body that has not at some time been in fashion. The arms, the breasts, the back, the whole figure have in turn been fully acknowledged. There is one exception, however. The English woman has for many generations refused to

confess to legs.' Nowadays, far from hiding legs, fashion and clothes can be used to enhance the natural shape of the body and above all, the legs.

It is important to know what type of clothes to choose to accentuate the good points of your legs and camouflage the bad points. If you have nice slim thighs, for example, you can get away with wearing fairly tight-fitting slacks or blue jeans. Women with heavy thighs, on the other hand, would be well advised to avoid wearing tight trousers. They will only emphasize the size of her thighs. Any material stretched tight across the flesh will make it look bigger, whether it is a pair of tight slacks or a bathing costume that cuts sharply into the top of the leg so that the thigh bulges out from under it. It is far better to select a light material that hangs loosely and naturally over the legs. This will give the impression of slimness.

From the knee down, disguise has to be slightly more convincing as it is this part of the leg that is most often revealed

to the world. Thick calves and ankles, for example, can be slimmed down by wearing dark stockings or tights, which should ideally tone with the shade of the shoes. Never wear socks that draw attention to a thick ankle and break the leg unattractively.

By sitting well you can display your legs to best advantage. If you do have heavy legs, there is no point in advertising the fact by spreading them out in all directions. It is much better to tuck them away neatly under your chair. If you have attractive legs that you are proud of, then do not spoil the effect by sitting badly. Always sit elegantly.

Apart from exercise to strengthen the legs and dieting to get rid of excess fat, there is a comparatively little that can be done to change a person's natural leg shape. By mastering the art of displaying your legs to their best advantage and by employing the skills of camouflage and illusion you can overcome many of the disadvantages of problem legs. There is no excuse for neglecting them.

Exercises for the Legs

Since your legs can be such a valuable beauty asset, it is well worth treating them with respect and lavishing the care and attention upon them that they merit. For beautiful legs are essentially strong and healthy legs—the products of a well-balanced diet, a good beauty-care programme and plenty of exercise.

Regular exercise is, in fact, one of the best ways of keeping your legs fit. Exercise has several beneficial effects on the legs. First it helps to slim them and then it helps to firm up the weak and flabby muscles, thus improving the shape and line of your legs.

Exercise—especially in the case of legs —is obviously a very broad term. After all, every time you walk around a room, run to catch a bus, or climb the stairs, you inevitably exercise your legs. The value of this everyday type of exercise should not be underestimated. Indeed, it can be exploited to the benefit of both your legs and your general health. A brisk walk or bicycle ride to work each day, or a walk in the park or in the country at the weekend can help to blow the cobwebs away as well as exercise your legs.

All these activities will help to tone your legs. There are also special leg exercises that you can do that will concentrate their effects on one area at a

time. Each of the following five exercises, for example, is designed to exercise a different part of the leg.

Before you start this exercise programme, examine your legs closely and critically in a full-length mirror and decide which part you especially want to improve. If heavy thighs are your weak point, for example, then concentrate your efforts on Exercise 4. It is best to work on one part of the leg at a time as you will be able to measure the progress you are making more quickly.

This does not mean, however, that you can afford to neglect the other parts of your legs. It is the proportions of the leg that draw admiring glances.

As with any exercise routine, the full benefits of these exercises will only really be felt if you persevere with them and practise them regularly. It helps to choose one particular time of the day, at bedtime or before breakfast and do them at the same time each day.

When you are exercising, always wear light clothes—a stretchy bra and pants are ideal, although a loose-fitting top and briefs or shorts are as suitable.

In addition to this comparatively energetic exercise routine, there are a variety of other, less strenuous leg exercises that you can practise virtually anywhere, at any convenient opportunity. While you are sitting reading your morning paper on the train, for example, you can be slimming your ankles. Start by rotating your ankles in a clockwise direction. Trace 10 circles with one foot and 10 with the other. Then change direction and do 10 circles with each foot in an anti-clockwise direction.

By combining these different types of exercise—the general walking-movement exercise, the planned exercise routine and the casual exercises—you will be giving your leg muscles the regular exercise they need to keep them lissome.

EXERCISE 1
Slims and strengthens the ankles

Sit on the floor with your legs straight out in front of you, supporting yourself on your hands placed just behind your hips on the floor. Keeping your right leg flat on the floor, kick your left leg up vigorously with a quick, jerking movement. It is like trying to touch and toss an imaginary pillow that is just out of your reach. You should point your toes really hard so that you feel this movement stretching your ankles and leg muscles. Repeat with your left leg, this time keeping your right leg flat on the floor.
Repeat 10 times at first, building up gradually to a total of 40 repetitions.

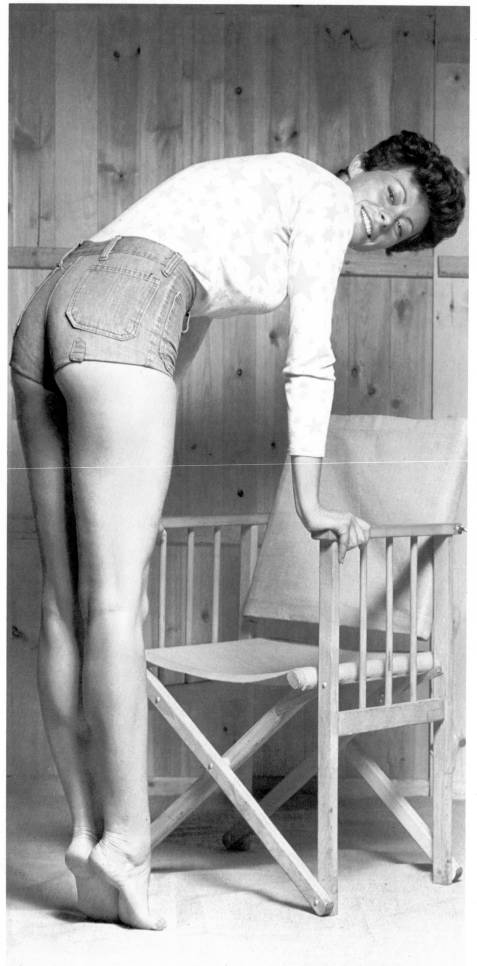

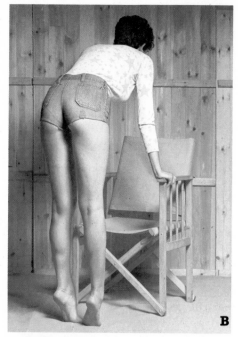

B

C

EXERCISE 2
Reduces the calves

A. Stand in front of a table or a chair with your feet together. Holding on to the edge of the table or chair, raise yourself up on to your toes. Stretch up as far as you can go until you are standing on the tip of your toes. Then slowly lower your heels to the floor again. Relax.

B. Repeat with your toes together and your ankles far apart.

C. Then repeat again, this time with your ankles together and your toes far apart.

Repeat each exercise eight times on the first day. Then add two extra repetitions each day until you reach 20.

A

EXERCISE 3
Slims fat knees

A. Lie on your back on the floor. Bend your knees, keeping your feet about four inches apart. Then suddenly bring your knees together and apart again in a sharp, slapping movement. Repeat 25 times.

B. Staying in the same position, do 25 bicycle kicks in the air. Stretch your left leg well up and bend your right leg sharply from the knee. Then in a pedalling motion, stretch your right leg up and bend your left leg down. Make sure that your arms are out to the side of your body and that your hips stay firmly on the floor throughout the exercise.

A

B

EXERCISE 4
Firms the fronts and backs of the thighs

A. Lie on the floor, flat on your back. Raise your right leg straight up in the air with your hands clasped around your thigh. Then pull your thigh back towards your face as far as you can, keeping your back and head on the floor all the time. Repeat with the left leg.
B. Now lie on your front and raise your right leg straight up behind you. Lift your leg as near to your head as you can. Repeat with the left leg.
Repeat each exercise five times and then relax.

EXERCISE 5
Helps to shape heavy legs

Lie on your right side, supporting your head on your right hand. Keeping your legs perfectly straight, raise your left leg to the mental count of five. Hold this position for another count of five before slowly lowering your leg again to a further count of five. Repeat twice on each side to start with, working up gradually to 20 repetitions.

Coping With Problem Veins

Will your legs always look smooth and shapely? Or will unsightly, knobbly veins mar their beauty while the rest of your body is still young and healthy-looking? Most young people think of varicose veins as an affliction of the elderly, but they can occur in the late teens and twenties. Since prevention is better than cure, it is best to understand what varicose veins are, what cause them and how they can be treated.

Basically, 'varicose' means abnormally dilated or swollen. Varicose veins, therefore, are so distended that they can be seen as knotty bulges just under the surface of the skin.

To understand how unsightly varicose veins occur, it helps to look closely at the venous, or vein system. This is a complex, but highly efficient network which regulates the flow of blood round the body.

Veins have valves in them which allow the blood to pass only in one direction. Each valve consists of two pouches which lie flat against the internal wall of the vein when the blood is flowing in the right direction but which open out to meet and block the passage when the blood tries to flow backwards. The legs have the greatest number of valves, followed by the arms; the internal organs

have only a few.

You can see where the valves are simply by rubbing your finger along a large vein in the arm or leg in the opposite direction to the blood flow. Little swellings will appear above each valve.

The veins have thinner walls than arteries, although their diameter is greater, to allow for the more leisurely flow of blood. The thinner walls, however, enable them to contract much more easily if less blood comes their way to keep the blood flowing properly. There is an imperceptible and continuous squeezing of the veins by muscles all over

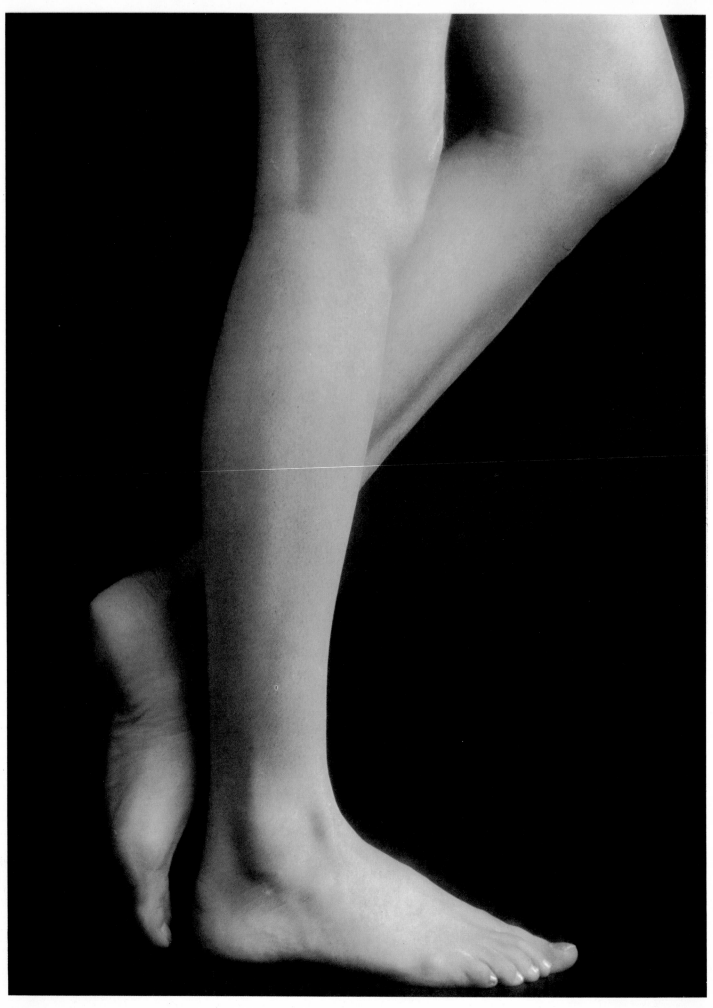

the body which keeps the blood flowing from valve to valve.

There are many more veins than arteries. Generally there are two veins working with each artery, except, strangely, with the largest artery which is 'partnered' by just one vein. The whole body is threaded with an intricate network of veins which collect blood from different areas of the body and drain it into other areas.

The legs are each served by one large vein—the inferior vena cava which is connected to two iliac veins. These collect blood from the abdomen and legs. The superficial veins drain into the external saphenous vein on the back of the leg and the internal saphenous veins which run from the instep up the inside of the leg and thigh. The system connected with the internal saphenous vein is the one that causes all the trouble, being especially liable to swell and become varicose.

The blood in the veins is blue because it does not contain oxygen. Oxygen is carried by haemoglobin. If there is no oxygen in your blood the haemoglobin turns blue. The veins are generally nearer the surface than the arteries so the blue blood is easily seen through the skin. This is why the term 'blue-blooded' is synonymous with the old European aristocracy. They led a sheltered, indoor life for the most part, and their veins, therefore, showed more clearly through their pale, thin-skinned hands, arms and necks giving the blue impression. The peasants and labourers, on the other hand, had rough, darkened skin because of their strenuous outdoor life.

Blood flow is stepped up with temperature and with exercise, so the veins have to expand to cope with the increase and to help the body maintain a reasonable temperature. Veins are nearer the surface and so you can see the swelling more easily, particularly in the veins on the back of the hands.

Because the blood flow in the veins in certain parts of the body can become very sluggish and because veins have weaker walls than arteries, they are particularly prone to disorders and inflammation.

The commonest of these is varicose veins. It is estimated that these occur in one woman out of two and one man in four over the age of 40, although they can occur in much younger people. Usually they are trivial, medically speaking, and many people never feel the need to have them treated. Sometimes, however, they are painful and usually they look ugly. Many women have them treated for purely cosmetic reasons.

It is the superficial saphenous veins near the surface of the leg which are usually affected. What happens is that the valves fail to work properly, causing

Shift your weight from one leg to the other and flex your toes to keep the blood flowing smoothly, especially when you are standing still during the day.

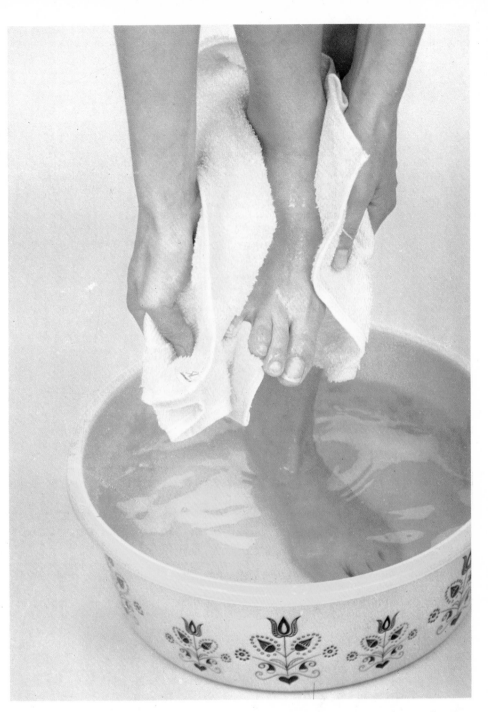

the blood to stagnate and the vein wall around the valve to swell. These swellings stand out as unsightly, knobbly protuberances on the skin's surface. There are many causes of varicose veins. Often the condition is hereditary. Some people are born with veins which are thinner-walled and weaker than others.

There are, however, many jobs which put people at greater-than-average risk of developing varicose veins. The danger comes in occupations which involve long periods of standing still when the muscular contractions of the legs are not properly at work to keep the blood flowing smoothly. Hairdressers, shop assistants and barmaids are particularly at risk. For men, dentistry is a particularly vulnerable profession.

The housewife could be in danger if she spent long hours standing still at the ironing board. But, as every housewife

Bathing your legs and feet in warm water stimulates the circulation of the blood, relieves pressure which builds up and reduces the likelihood of swelling veins.

knows, her job also involves a great deal of moving about so she would rarely suffer from varicose veins in this way. Sometimes after long waits in shopping lines or at bus-stops, a housewife may experience a feeling of tiredness or throbbing in her legs and even swelling about the ankles.

Even the slightest movement of the legs helps the blood flow, so if you do have to stand for a long time, it is a good idea just to flex your toes occasionally, or shift your weight from your toes to your heel or vice versa. A few minutes' rest with your feet up (ideally above the heart level) should relieve the pressure on the veins of your legs and quickly restore them to normal. It is important to remember that varicose veins do not point to anything very serious. Regular exercise will help to make sure that your blood keeps moving.

In addition to the knotty bumps, symptoms of varicose veins include a feeling of weariness and tiredness in the legs and swollen ankles. In severe cases the valve failure can lead to a 'water-logged' skin which is discoloured because of continuous leakage of small amounts of blood and fluid from the blood vessels. These areas can become very itchy and are prone to ulcers even after the smallest injury. The vein can also become inflamed, a condition known as phlebitis.

Pregnancy can be a contributory cause, although the condition frequently disappears after the baby is born. Constipation, too, puts pressure on the venous system by partially blocking veins in the pelvic area.

The veins affected by varicosities are generally not the deep ones in the leg, but the saphenous veins near the surface of the skin. This means that they are easily accessible for simple surgery or they can be blocked by injecting an irritant which encourages the vein walls to collapse and stick together or blocks them with a blood clot. These artificial clots are not dangerous because they adhere firmly to the vein's walls.

The commonest operation for varicose veins is 'stripping'. The vein is tied off at two places and the intervening swollen part literally stripped out en masse. Although the operation is a simple one, it does carry a very small risk of complications and involves a few days' stay in hospital. An increasing number of doctors are following the more modern injection techniques which seem just as effective and which are far quicker and cheaper to carry out.

The modern method is properly known as injection-compression sclerotherapy and consists of a series of injections—usually about seven in all. A small quantity of detergent-like fluid known as a sclerosant is injected and causes the vein to collapse. The leg is tightly bandaged to accelerate the process. Injections are repeated each week until all the varicosities have subsided.

Many surgeons, however, still believe in the less sophisticated stripping operations. The reason for this may well be that exaggerated claims of a total 'cure' were made when injection techniques were first introduced. Neither surgery nor injection can 'cure' varicose veins because they do not attack the underlying causes. Unfortunately varicosities can reappear after either method, but weight control and regular exercise can help keep them at ease.

Phlebitis can be a cause for concern when it is associated with a blood clot in a larger, deeper vein. The clot can break away and pass through the heart to lodge in a branch of the main artery, cutting off the blood supply to part of the lungs.

This blocking is called pulmonary embolism and is a major cause of unexpected death after surgical operations because the manipulation of organs during surgery, and the complete bed rest afterwards encourages the formation of clots, called thrombosis, in the veins nearby. For this reason, surgical patients are always given special exercises soon after their operation, to make sure there is no blood stagnation and clotting.

It has also been shown that oral contraceptives carry a tiny increased risk of blood-clotting. They are not recommended for women with a family history of, or a tendency to, blood clotting disease. Normally, however, the blood clots formed in the veins are reabsorbed into the blood stream.

Haemorrhoids, commonly known as piles, are also a form of distended or varicose veins. Again this seems to be an evolutionary penalty, as the main cause of the trouble seems to be pressure from the abdominal muscles on the veins running up the lining of the rectum. The veins in this area are particularly prone to trouble. The muscles which keep the rectum closed interfere with circulation through the haemorrhoidal veins. It appears that hereditary factors play a part in this condition.

Doctors believe that some people's

By controlling your weight and taking regular exercise you will ensure that your veins function adequately and more efficiently.

---

habits and diet make them more vulnerable. This ailment is especially common in men with sedentary jobs who do not take enough exercise and, because of the extra pressure, it is more likely to occur in men and women who are overweight. Piles are fairly common in the younger age groups, too.

Habitual constipation is a significant factor in this condition although it is unlikely to be the sole cause. The discomfort of haemorrhoids encourages constipation, so the two complaints aggravate each other in a particularly vicious circle. Sitting on a cold or damp surface—or even a general chill—can inflame already swollen veins and bring on what is commonly known as 'an attack of piles'. Women often suffer from piles during pregnancy although they usually recede after the child is born.

The risk of haemorrhoids can be reduced by sensible eating and a reasonable amount of regular exercise. Exercise helps carry the blood off the limbs and so prevent a build up of pressure in the veins. Obesity creates many other problems as well as piles, so it is important to keep to a well-balanced diet to prevent you from gaining extra pounds. Constipation can be avoided by eating plenty of fruit and vegetables every day. Excessive alcoholic drinks and strong

purgatives should be avoided because they can actually help to bring on the condition by irritating the delicate tissues.

One of the main symptoms of haemorrhoids is bleeding. Although there may be some discomfort—and much embarrassment—piles are rarely painful. But if they last a long time, even a small amount of blood lost each day can rob the body's supplies of iron and lead to anaemia. It is most important that you seek prompt medical advice about piles. In some cases the symptoms of piles are similar to more serious illnesses. It is best to be safe and comfortable rather than sick and sorry.

Small haemorrhoids can often be cured by suppositories designed to reduce congestion and by mild laxatives. Special ointments are available on the market to reduce itching and careful regular washing with warm water is always recommended by doctors. Soap, however, can act as an irritant.

For more serious cases, injection techniques or surgery are used. The injection method is slightly different from that used in the leg. Here, the irritant fluid is used to cause scarring around the haemorrhoid. In surgery the offending veins may be removed or isolated and tied off with ligatures.

Even broken veins are occasionally seen on the face, especially around the nose, and on the back of the hands. These are caused by failure in the mechanism which controls the dilation or constriction of the blood vessels. Frequently this breakdown is caused by an excessive intake of alcohol although there are other causes, including the natural process of aging.

Alcohol makes the blood vessels expand particularly just beneath the skin's surface. When they dilate you become flushed and feel a rosy glow. If an individual were continually to drink to excess, the tiny capillary blood vessels would 'jam' in the distended position. This in turn can create problems at the venous end of the capillary system by causing the tiny blood vessels to rupture and adding a fine tracery of broken veins to the crimson hue.

Going from a hot atmosphere into the cold puts extra strain on the control mechanisms. So again 'moderation in all things' is the best method of prevention. There is as yet no cure for broken veins. It is often quite simple, however, for both men and women to disguise the offending vessels with special preparations should they prove embarrassing.

Generally, however, the veins function remarkably well in coping with all the pressures put upon them. Knowing even a little about how they work can show you how you can help them to perform their tasks more efficiently. The secret, as with all aspects of healthy living, lies in a commonsense approach to life—enough but not too much—of the right kinds of foods and regular, though not necessarily strenuous, exercise.

Care for Your Arms

Most of us take our arms very much for granted. Admittedly, they are very useful and we would be lost without them, but actually caring for our arms in a conscious way hardly seems necessary. However, arms can be a beautiful as well as a useful part of the anatomy. They can be graceful, expressive, good to look at and good to touch. Long, slim arms with soft skin, firm muscles and delicate wrists are very much a beauty asset, particularly when they are revealed by well-cut sleeveless blouses, sweaters and evening dresses.

To begin with, it is important to understand the basic structure of your arms. The bones of the arms form a remarkable piece of practical engineering. The long, upper bone stretches between the shoulder joint and the elbow. At the upper end it articulates

neatly with the shoulder girdle at the shoulder joint to enable us to move our arms forwards, backwards, sideways and in circular movements. From the knobbly elbow joint, two slightly shorter lower bones stretch to the wrist. They can be twisted over one another so that the palm of the hand can face upwards or downwards. At the wrist, eight small, irregular-shaped bones fit very closely together to make a very flexible region indeed. If you move your wrists about loosely, you will feel just how flexible they are—and it is worth considering just what an asset this is for activities like playing the piano, typing, painting or even waving.

Five main sets of muscles are concerned with arm movement. They are grouped around the bones to push and pull them into action and to give the familiar shape to the arms. Flabby muscles tend to attract fat. This is particularly true of the upper arm muscles: the brachialis, which stretch across the front of the lower part of the upper arms, and the triceps and biceps, which stretch across the back and the front of the upper part of the upper arms.

Unfortunately, these muscles are not used as much as the wrist flexors and wrist extensors, which stretch along the front and back of the forearms. Flabby forearms are not nearly as common as flabby upper arms. But how many of us can say that activities such as digging, shovelling earth and weight-lifting are part of our daily routine? These are the kind of activities which exercise those fat-prone upper arm muscles. Anyone who has a weight problem in this area must exercise. There are some very effective exercises which form a practical substitute for the very infrequent 'heavy duty' activities.

Have you really looked at your arms lately? If the answer is yes, then you probably mean that you have looked at the front or possibly the sides of your arms—but probably not the backs. Try studying a close, all-round view of your arms by using two mirrors.

Sit or stand comfortably, facing a large wall mirror or dressing-table mirror, about an arm's distance away. Stretch out both arms in front of you and study them directly, and look at their reflection in the mirror.

Examine the texture of the skin closely. Is the skin smooth and soft, or hard and flaky or scaly? Are the backs of the upper arms mottled-looking, bluish in tone? Is the crease at the front of the elbow joint dry and very lined?

Now look at the shape of your arms. Are the forearms and wrists slim and narrow or do the forearms bulge just before the elbow joint? Are the upper arms bulging or slim? When the elbow is bent at an angle of 45°, do 'handles' of flesh appear each side of the joint?

Now take a small hand-mirror in your right hand, raise your left arm slightly and hold the mirror below the left elbow at such an angle that the elbow and upper part of the back of the arm are clearly visible in the mirror.

Again examine the skin-texture. Study your elbow. Is it knobbly, rough and dry-looking? Is the bone very red-looking? Is the back of the upper arm near the shoulder tough and rather pitted just like orange peel?

Look at the shape as well. Does the upper arm form one slim, straight line, or is it bulging slightly or a great deal from the top of the elbow to the shoulder joint?

Repeat these observations for the right upper arm. Now, turn sideways-on to the mirror, left arm closest to it with the arm hanging straight. Take the small mirror in the right hand and study the arm from the side view.

First check the silhouette. Does the arm form a smooth, slim line or is there an ugly bulge of dry flesh at the elbow, and another ugly bulge just above it? Are the shoulders round or straight?

Then look for unwanted hair. Can you see small 'whiskers' of underarm hair appearing at the front of the arm, even though you were sure that these had been thoroughly removed?

Repeat these observations for the right arm.

If this close-up study revealed more arm beauty problems than you previously realized, do not despair. It is better to recognize the problem, and then to tackle it sensibly than to go around completely oblivious of the ugliness that is on clear view to other people. It simply underlines the fact that, in beauty, vigilance and observation are vital— whatever your age. Here is a guide to treating those problems, from the shoulders downwards.

Round shoulders
If your arms hang forwards from rounded shoulder joints, then this one simple defect can mar your appearance in a sleeveless dress. From the front, your reflection in the mirror may look fine— from the side, you can be assured that it certainly does not. Unfortunately, rounded shoulders often start in childhood with bad posture and slouching at school. The developing bones become set abnormally forward in the shoulder girdle and this unnatural development is probably never corrected. However, fast improvements can be made if you are determined to straighten things out. This should start with an awareness of correct walking and sitting posture, and continue the good work by doing some very simple posture exercises in the privacy of your bedroom.

Underarm hygiene
The large concentration of sweat glands under the arms is responsible for underarm odour. Regular, twice-daily washing and the use of a good deodorant can generally overcome this problem. If underarm perspiration is persistent despite these simple precautions, stronger measures can be taken, including discarding badly-stained or sour-smelling clothing, using impregnated deodorant pads frequently during the day, and even having the sweat glands removed surgically.

Unwanted hair
It is also important to remove unwanted underarm hair in winter and in summer. Bacteria becomes trapped in this hair, so getting rid of it is a good way to tackle offensive odour as well as an unsightly problem. Always wash and dry the area before removing hair and never apply a deodorant product to freshly shaved or creamed skin.

Flabby upper arms
Unwanted extra flesh on the upper arms is a common problem. Sometimes, the flesh is pitted and coarse in texture like orange peel. This condition is caused by accumulations of cellulite and is different from fat, but it does respond to exercise and fairly tough massage. If you have unwanted extra inches in this area, begin by making bathtime a regular underwater 'massage' treatment. Keeping your left upper arm under the water, pinch the flesh very firmly between the first finger and thumb of the right hand. Do this all over the flabby area, and repeat with the other arm.

Supplement a regular daily exercise routine with slightly increased work for those flabby upper arm muscles. Gardening will help firm them up, so will lifting and carrying fairly heavy objects. But remember not to strain some other part of your body in the process.

Mottled upper arms
Bad circulation can give the upper arms a mottled appearance. It is possible to correct this by giving the skin a brisk rub with a loofah or friction glove at bathtime, and following up with alternate hot and cold douches. A little Epsom salts added to the bathwater will help to stimulate the circulation.

It is unwise to submit arms to violent changes in temperature if you have this problem. Hugging an open fire in winter, then dashing out into a cold corridor is very bad for the appearance of your skin. Try to keep your arms at a fairly constant temperature by adding or removing clothing as necessary.

Rough upper arms
Little 'whiteheads' and rough patches sometimes disfigure the upper arms. Acidity in the skin causes whiteheads to appear. First, stimulate the circulation as described above. Then treat the blemishes by patting almond or olive oil on the affected area, and wrapping it in a hot towel for a few moments. The whiteheads will loosen and can be

extracted using an ordinary blackhead extractor, which is rather like a tiny metal spoon with a hole in the bowl. It may be necessary to get a friend to do this in difficult areas of the backs of the arms, but by using two mirrors it should be possible to operate the extractor oneself. Treat roughness by nourishing the skin just as you would do your face. Use a good moisturizing cream after the bath and bathe the skin regularly with a solution of one part cider vinegar to eight parts water. (This is also good for elbows.)

Dry cracked elbows
Red, rough elbows are extremely unsightly but unfortunately they are very common. One of the oldest and most effective treatments for this is to lean elbows in lemon halves at any opportunity. Keeping a lemon, cut in half, by the kitchen 'sink is a good idea—then, when sleeves are already rolled up for other tasks, the lemon treatment can be quickly used. Lemons definitely do have a softening and whitening effect on this area.

It is a good idea to rub handcream up your arms and into the elbows every time you use it for your hands. Making this a habit is a simple but effective beauty treatment for this area. If the elbows become chapped and sore, an infusion of marigold petals in water added to a mixture of rosewater and glycerine will make a soothing, natural cream. But do ask your doctor for a more effective ointment if the trouble persists.

Weak wrists
Wrist strength is a useful asset; neat wrists are a fine beauty point. Both can be acquired with exercise and use, Many people who type, paint or play the piano find that their wrists become strong and supple naturally. For others, such strength and suppleness can only be attained through exercises.

Make-up and disguise
Prominent veins and blotchy skin may still mar the beauty of your arms on special occasions—even if the shape and texture are improved by the treatment.

Some cosmetic houses produce special leg make-up which can equally well be used on the arms. However, this must be applied carefully and evenly using a damp sponge—and contact with clothing must be avoided as much as possible, otherwise it may tend to rub off.

A careful application of compressed translucent powder over moisturizing cream will enhance arm beauty for special occasions, too. A stick of covering make-up should first be applied to 'problem areas' such as veins and blotches.

You will soon find that your arms respond well to this combination of extra beauty care and exercise, and that they gradually become more graceful and more attractive.

POSTURE ROUTINE

Exercise 1
Wear a sleeveless dress or sweater for this exercise. Thread a ruler or other straight piece of smooth wood or cane through the armholes and across the tops of your shoulders. This will force you to keep your shoulders well back. Leave the ruler in place while you are watching television, knitting or reading.

Exercise 2
Sit comfortably, with your back straight and your hands clasped lightly in your lap. Rotate your right shoulder backwards. Keep your back very straight and your arms as still as possible throughout the exercise. Continue for about one minute. Repeat with your left shoulder and then with both shoulders together.

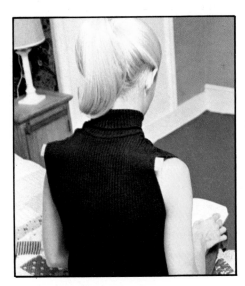

Exercise 3
Stand up straight, with your feet slightly apart and your arms held straight out to the side, at right angles to your body. Swing your arms backwards—singly at first and then together. Continue for a few minutes.

MUSCLE-TONING ROUTINE

Exercise 1
Stand with your back to the bathroom or bedroom wall, about one foot away. Place the palms of your hands flat against it. Press hard, holding the contraction for a count of six. You should feel the tension in your upper arms. Repeat six times.

Exercise 2
Stand sideways to the wall, an arm's distance away. Place the palm of your nearest hand flat against it. Push against the wall hard, holding the contraction for a count of six. Relax.
Repeat six times with one arm and then do the whole exercise again with the other arm.

Exercise 3
Sit comfortably on a bathroom stool or bed, with your back straight. Hold a large aerosol can of deodorant or hair spray between your hands, with your arms held straight out in front of you. Squeeze hard on the ends of the can and then try to push your hands together. Hold the contraction for a count of six. Repeat six times.

WRIST-STRENGTHENING
ROUTINE

Exercise 1
Imagine you are playing the piano. Press your fingers firmly down on a table. Then raise and lower each finger almost as if you were practising a musical 'scale'. Press each finger down very firmly indeed, holding your wrists poised above the table.

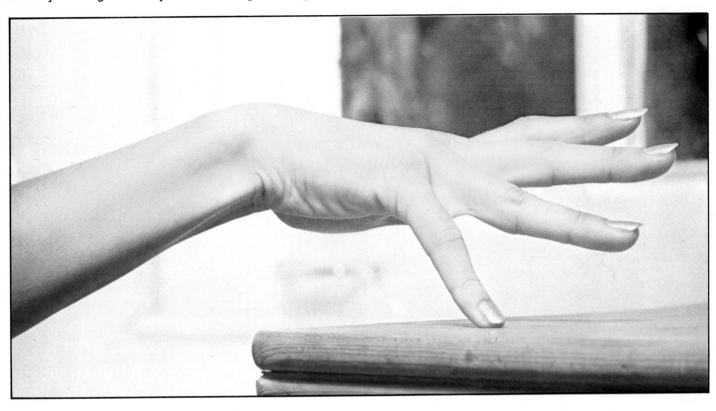

Exercise 2
Hold a small, heavy object such as a paperweight in your right hand. Now rotate your hand from the wrist outwards and then inwards. Continue for a few minutes. Transfer the weight to your left hand and repeat, flexing your wrist as far as you can.

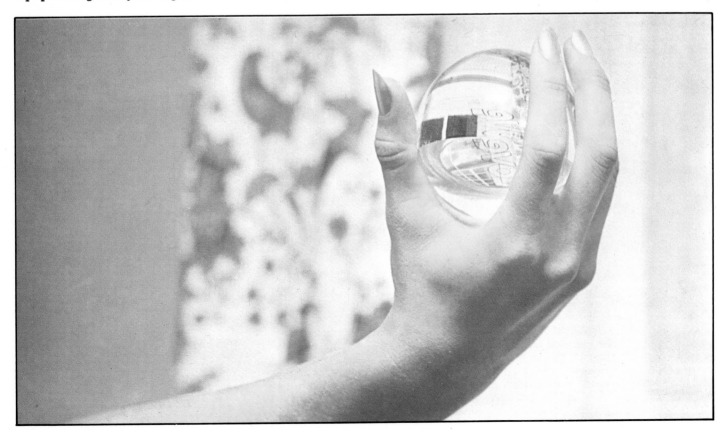

Care for Your Feet

Neglect your feet and it shows—on your face. Sadly, one of the most useful parts of the human anatomy is also one of the least well cared-for. Most people wait until foot troubles become unbearable before tackling the problem. But a little thought and careful choice of shoes can ensure that you do not suffer any of the unpleasant symptoms of foot neglect.

It is a pity that feet are so unloved, because beautiful, shapely ankles and perfectly formed toes can be as attractive as pretty hands. Feet are covered for most of the year, so the appeal of smooth, pampered feet is often forgotten. In summer, however, it is a different story for feet are on show. Open sandals or the bare-foot look on the beach can reveal a lifetime of neglect. Fortunately, although it is wisest to begin foot care in childhood, it is never too late to start looking after your feet.

Children's feet

The kicking enjoyed by tiny babies is their first foot and ankle exercises—and it helps to make feet and legs strong. (Mothers should never tuck bedclothes in so tightly that their baby cannot kick and bootees should be loose enough to allow toes to wriggle freely.) At birth, a child's feet consist of soft, small bones which do not become hardened fully until he or she is about 18 years old.

Tight nylon socks, badly-fitting shoes and slippers—even tight ballet pumps—all can help to deform the soft bones. Many children have wide feet and broad toes, so it is essential to measure width as well as length when fitting new shoes. A child should never wear rubber boots all day as these are very bad for the feet. They do not support the arch of the foot and could lead to flat feet later on. Another taboo is the slip-on type of shoe which has no support across the top or around the ankle. The natural action of the child is to curl his toes under to hold on the shoe, and this can result in permanently bent toes. To give feet maximum freedom for correct growth, small children should be allowed to go barefoot as much as possible in the house, on the beach or in the garden.

Teenagers' feet

As feet grow, they change their shape and proportion. It is, therefore, vital to continue checking foot measurements well into the teens before buying shoes. Fashion can be a big help—or hindrance —to healthy foot development in this age-group. Very narrow, pointed shoes and shoes with very high heels are extremely bad for teenage feet since the toes are squashed down into the front of the shoe and deformed in the process. Flatter shoes with a wide toe section are·

better, provided there is sufficient support on the instep.

One of the chief dangers for growing teenagers is foot infection. Verrucae are sometimes picked up in swimming pools or communal showers, and athlete's foot, which is caused by a fungus growth attacking the feet, can be contracted in places where warm, moist conditions lower skin resistance. Infections like these need professional treatment by a doctor or chiropodist, as they can be painful and also tend to spread if not caught at an early stage.

Adults' feet

It is hard to imagine yourself unable to go out to the shops because your feet are too painful to take you there, but this does happen to very many old people. And the main cause is usually neglect in the middle years of life. Bad shoes, tight socks or stockings and lack of general cleanliness and care can cause all kinds of problems.

Basic foot care involves keeping feet scrupulously clean, cutting toe-nails regularly and lavishing a little of the attention you normally pay to your hands to your feet as well.

If chilblains are your problem, massage your feet gently with a foot oil or lanolin. In hot weather use a special foot deodorant spray and put talcum powder in your shoes to prevent odour. Rinse stockings or tights nightly or wear clean socks every day. Never roast your feet over the fire in winter or sleep with your feet on a hot water bottle; these are the most common causes of chilblains.

After an exceptionally tiring day, 'paddle' your feet in cold, salted water. This is better than the traditional mustard bath which softens the skin too much. After bathing, always dry your feet carefully between the toes. And choose your slippers carefully, do not wear casual 'mules' all day, they don't give enough arch support.

For every day, choose shoes that allow your toes to move freely, and that grip the heel and instep firmly. When buying shoes, walk up and down in the shop several times before deciding if they fit properly and are comfortable. Shoes should not have to be worn in, they should fit straight away. Beware of wooden-soled shoes as these can be harmful to the arch of the foot.

Don't be brave about minor foot ailments, be sensible instead. Chiropodists spend much of their time sorting out problems caused by their patients' attempts at self-medication, the damage done can be very grave indeed. Never poke at corns or hard skin with a razor, nail file or other unsterilized instrument. Don't use corn solvents yourself or

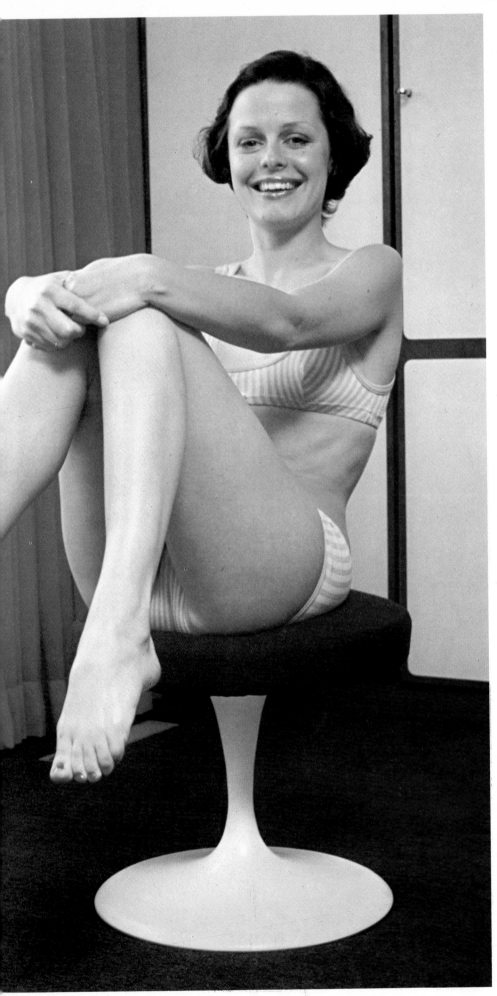

attempt to apply a lambs' wool protection for the toe as this can easily restrict circulation. A 15-minute foot check-up twice a year is an excellent idea. And if corns, callouses or more serious foot ailments develop, then professional treatment is essential.

Chiropody has a 'middle-aged' image —but young people too can benefit tremendously from the services of a good chiropodist. Don't think that a single, nagging corn is too unimportant for you to take professional advice about. It is better to deal with minor problems as they occur than to suffer for 20 years and then present a chiropodist with a full range of foot ailments.

Exercises For The Feet

EXERCISE 1
Strengthens ankles.

Sit on a stool or the edge of the bed. Raise your legs and bend your knees, clasping your hands round your knees for support. Now rotate your feet first outwards and then inwards. Repeat for a few minutes.

EXERCISE 2
Strengthens ankles.

In the same position as 1 point your toes alternately upwards and downwards. Repeat 30 times.

1   2

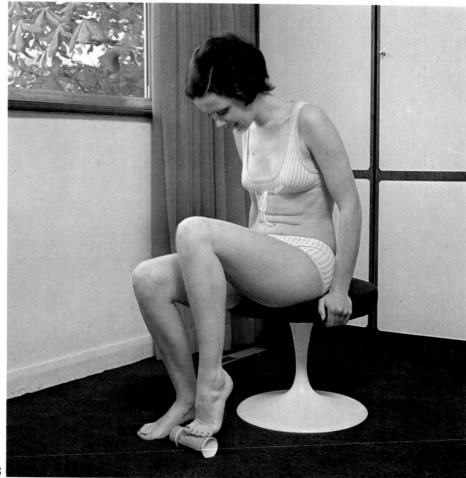

3

4

EXERCISE 3
Strengthens toes and arches.

In a standing position throw a light
scarf or handkerchief in the air and
keep it there by kicking with
alternate feet. Repeat 10 times or
until tired.

EXERCISE 4
Strengthens arches and balls
of feet.

Sit on a stool or the edge of the bed.
Place a cylinder such as an aerosol
can of hair-spray on the floor. Put
your right foot on the can and roll it
backwards and forwards from the
tips of the toes to the heel. Now use
the left foot. Repeat five times with
each foot.

EXERCISE 5
Strengthens toes and ankles.

Sit on the floor, with your knees
bent and your back straight. Clasp
your right foot with your right hand
and your left foot with your left
hand. Now raise left and right feet
alternately in a scissors movement.
Repeat 10 times.

5

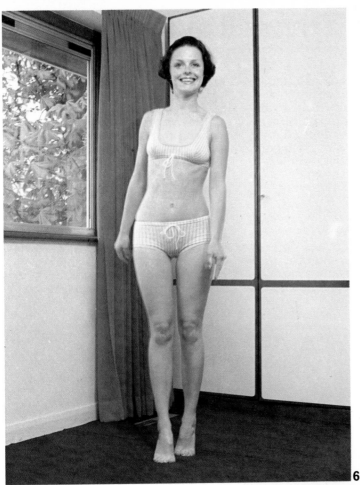
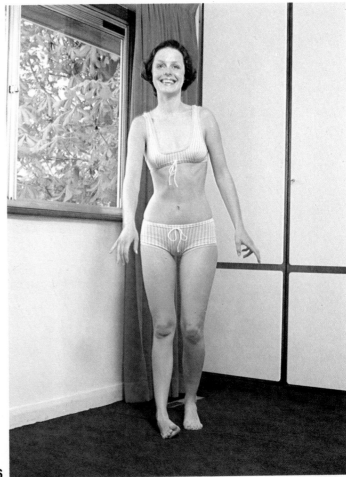

6

6

EXERCISE 6
Increases circulation and strengthens feet and ankles.

Stand at one end of the room. Take four paces on tip-toe, four on your heels, four on the inside of your feet, four on the outside. Relax and walk backwards in the same way.

EXERCISE 7
Relaxes feet and legs when tired.

Lie on your back with your legs up against the wall. Try to form a right-angle with your legs and your body. Stay in this position until you feel refreshed.

7

Give Yourself A Pedicure

Well-groomed toenails and smooth healthy feet make for an attractive appearance generally. Follow this step-by-step pedicure and in less than half an hour your feet will be worthy of display. Before you begin, get all your equipment together. You will need: paper tissues, cotton wool balls, nail clippers, emery boards, orange sticks, nail varnish, varnish remover and massage cream. Make sure you are sitting in a comfortable position on a chair or on the edge of the bath, with your foot placed firmly on a stool in front of you. Follow each step carefully. Male readers can give themselves a pedicure too.

1. NAIL TRIMMING
With a pair of nail clippers, clip nails straight across, and keep them short. Long toenails never look good and can cause foot problems.

2. NAIL FILING
With the fine-grained side of an emery board (usually lighter in colour) smooth down any rough edges. Always file in the same direction.

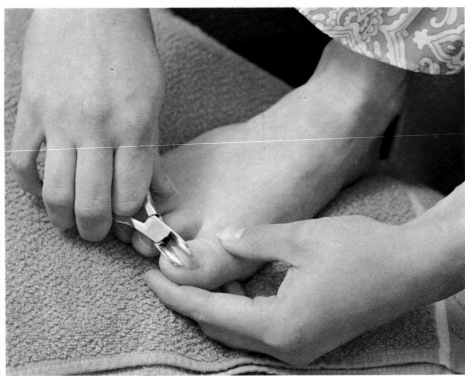

1

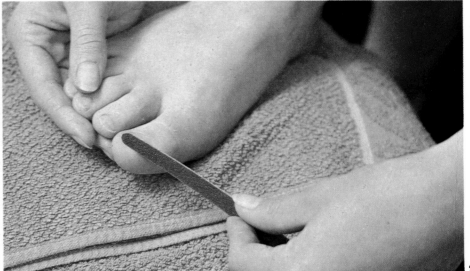

2

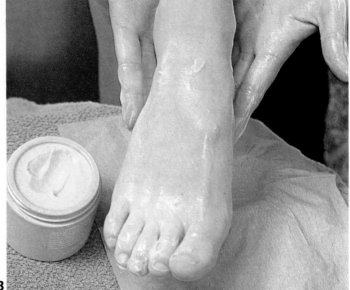

3. HARD SKIN FILING
With the rough-grained side of an emery board smooth away rough skin.

4. FOOT MASSAGE
Rub a generous amount of vitamin or massage cream all over the foot in smooth strokes away from the toes, on top and underneath. Wipe off any surplus with a tissue.

5. CUTICLE MASSAGE
Place some cream on each toenail and work it into the cuticles with an orange stick, easing the skin away from the nails.

6. POLISH—BASE COAT
Place a small piece of cotton wool in between each toe to separate them. Then apply base coat starting with the big toe.

7. POLISH—TOP COAT
Apply nail polish in three distinct strokes, working from the base of the nail up and outwards. Re-apply after 10 minutes.

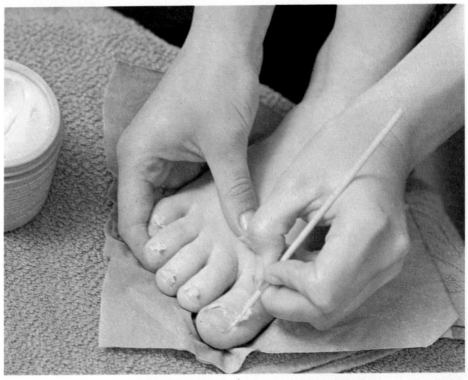

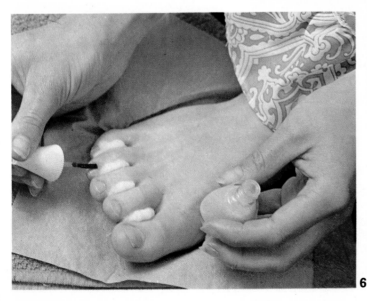

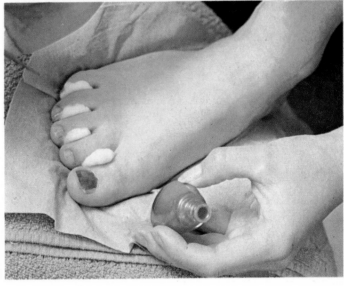

Care for Your Hands

Beautiful, smooth hands reveal a great deal about a personality. They can indicate fastidious attention to detail, a love of good grooming and cleanliness and some people even consider that they reveal gentleness and an artistic nature. It is certainly true that well-cared-for hands are noticed and admired even if they are not the classically perfect shape.

Hands tend to show up so much in everyday life and work that they are bound to be noticed. The executive who looks over his secretary's shoulder to check a letter she is typing sees not her carefully combed hair or beautiful long legs, but her hands. The customer waiting patiently at the bank does not watch the clock, he watches the clerk's hands.

For many people, hand care is constantly necessary because their hands are expected to work so hard. Hairdressers, typists, manual workers of all kinds—these are the people who must be especially vigilant about caring for their hands. Troubles such as stiffness, soreness and infections like dermatitis can be painful as well as unattractive. Although the skin of the hands is tough—it has to be—it cannot be expected to emerge unscathed from experiences such as almost constant immersion in water that contains harsh chemical additives, daily contact with dirty metal, prolonged, shuddering pressure. A hairdresser or pneumatic drill operator subjects her or his hands to just this kind of abuse all the time and should therefore take extra precautions to protect their hands.

The physical structure of the hands is delicate and fascinating. Eighteen bones form the hand, fingers and thumb. Five long bones, side by side, form the palm of the hand, then five slightly smaller bones connected to these form the lower part of the fingers and thumb. Five slightly smaller bones form the next part of the fingers and the tip of the thumb. Finally, four very small bones form the tips of the fingers. At each joint, the hand and finger bones can move freely and give the amazing flexibility of the hands which we all take for granted.

The large joints between the fingers and the five bones which form the palms of the hands are very much more pronounced and are called the knuckles. The knuckles have to be tough. Man's instinctive defensive action is to clench his fist, ready to throw a punch with those tough knuckle bones.

Clever co-ordination between brain, muscle and bones means that our hands can move quickly and accurately to perform the tasks we dictate. But like any efficient, complex piece of machinery, the hands do need care to do their job properly—quite apart from care, to look good. There are tried-and-tested remedies for dealing with a number of specific hand problems. Remember to tackle each problem as soon as it arises. Do not let your hands suffer unnecessarily—for they really are very hard working indeed, and deserve your care and attention.

There is much that can be done to prevent roughness. The skin covering the hands is tough—but not indestructible. You can prevent roughness from developing by using a good lubricating hand cream at night and in the morning and after every immersion in water.

Wear rubber gloves for washing dishes and sprinkle talcum powder inside them to keep them fresh-smelling. If water trickles inside the gloves, dry them thoroughly before wearing them again. Should a hand infection develop, it would be unwise to wear them at all. You could re-infect yourself by doing so. The best thing is to ask your doctor's advice. If you have to tackle a particularly dirty job for which rubber gloves would be far too cumbersome, then try wearing thin cotton gloves instead. Be careful to avoid bringing your hands into contact with harsh chemical cleansing agents such as scouring powder, lavatory cleanser, detergents, liquid polishes and metal polish.

Many men find it very difficult indeed to wear gloves to do a dirty job. Barrier creams can be used instead to help prevent roughness from developing and, very important, they can stop dirt from becoming ingrained in the pores of the skin. Harsh scrubbing to remove dirt is undesirable. The dirt is looser and easier to remove with a barrier cream.

If roughness and soreness does develop, then try one of the following softening treatments.

Cover your hands with a mixture of 4 tablespoons of glycerine to half a cup of rosewater. Put on cotton gloves and sleep in them. Next morning, wash off the residue with a very mild soap, rub in hand cream thoroughly.

Cover your hands with a mixture of 2 tablespoons of almond oil, 1 teaspoon of honey and the yolk of an egg. Wear cotton gloves for an hour or so. Remove the gloves and wash your hands in a mixture of vinegar and water.

An inexpensive softening treatment which is most effective is cocoa butter which, although a trifle greasy, does remove rough skin. Apply it very thinly.

You can prevent the rough condition from worsening by keeping your hands warm in cold weather. Wear gloves but avoid nylon, which tends to hamper the skin from breathing, or mittens. Keep your circulation healthy by exercising your hands as much as possible. Try to keep your hands out of water as much as possible until the condition improves.

Eczema

This is a rough skin condition on the hands and arms, sometimes found on other parts of the body too, which is often triggered off by nervous tension. The condition is particularly irritating since it seems to strike at most inconvenient times when nervous tension is high—for example before a wedding, an exam or important interview.

It can sometimes be helped by increasing the intake of the B vitamins (especially Vitamin B_{12}) in your diet. Liver, yeast and wheatgerm are foods containing a high concentration of the vitamin B complex. Try a teaspoon of powdered yeast five or six times a day as a food supplement. If you suffer from eczema, do seek your doctor's advice as he may recommend some kind of psychotherapy which is often very effective.

Chilblains

Frequently these are the result of poor circulation. This is largely responsible for the roughness and soreness of painful chilblains. The first essential is to keep your hands warm, so wear gloves with soft, wool linings to give double insulation. Keep your circulation healthy with special exercises and avoid sudden changes in temperature. Never sit very close to the fire or plunge your hands into very hot water.

Do not subject your hands to very cold temperatures, for example, handling frozen foods then warming your hands at a heater. Use a good antiseptic ointment on the affected area at night and wear cotton gloves on top. Wash your hands in tepid water and dry very thoroughly indeed. Moisture can worsen the condition.

Perspiration

Clammy, sweaty hands can be an embarrassing problem particularly if you are dealing with people all day long by shaking hands, holding hands or touching hands. It is a problem which is largely caused by nervous tension. It happens to most of us at some time or other, but for some people it happens too often for comfort.

The sweat glands on the palms of the hands are the eccrine type, which secrete 99% water, 1% inorganic salts and do not attract odour-forming bacteria. Moisture is trapped in this area when it is secreted from surrounding glands. The palms form a natural 'basin' for the moisture to collect. Because it is usually exposed to the air, the trapped moisture will eventually evaporate, no bacteria will be formed and odour is negligible.

If you do have sweaty palms, make

sure that your gloves are porous, wool or cotton, to allow the moisture to escape freely. Wash your hands regularly with a fresh smelling soap and keep a supply of cologne-impregnated tissues at work or school for quick refreshing wipes between washing. These tissues can be used without drawing attention to your problem.

Keep the rest of your body and your mental approach cool in difficult situations. Try to acquire confidence in your work, opinions and actions. Be fastidious about all aspects of personal hygiene, not only your hands, so that you can be confident that you are pleasant to be near. Avoid clenching your hands in moments of tension. Make yourself keep your hands flat on the table, since simply clenching them does help trap annoying excess moisture.

Because hands work so hard, they are vulnerable to cuts and bruises. If you are 'all thumbs' when it comes to a tricky job, then you have probably had your fair share of minor hand injuries, and you know how inconvenient and painful they can be. This is how to treat those awkward injuries and avoid them occurring again:

Cuts between the fingers
These are particularly dangerous because they can sometimes cause lockjaw. Get in touch with your doctor immediately in case stitches are necessary. Always try to handle instruments with a sharp or jagged metal edge—for example opened food cans, rusty tins and garden tools, with great care.

Bruised fingers
Doors slamming on fingers or hammers brought down on them should be treated immediately. Check a badly bruised finger or thumb to make absolutely sure there are no bones broken. Rest it for a while in a sling, if you are tempted to use it, then exercise it a little at a time until the bruising disappears. The next time you use nails and hammer, lightly tap the nail in place and save the big thump for the moment when the nail is able to stay in place without the aid of your fingers.

Cut or grazed knuckles are sometimes slow to heal since the skin across the knuckle is stretched taut every time the hand is bent. Bandage the cut so the hand is forced to remain straight until healing is well under way. Avoid walking too close to rough walls which could scrape this part of your hand.

Cut fingertips should be washed and bathed with antiseptic, then use a protective covering until they have healed. Some improbable materials can cause this type of cut—a sheet of paper, a blade of grass, a piece of sewing thread or string.

Warts
These are caused by multiplication of skin cells which may be triggered off by rough skin or an infection. They are notoriously stubborn to get rid of—and old wives' tales abound on methods for their 'magical' destruction. If you have one—or a crop—of these unsightly skin growths, do not fiddle around with them. The recognized form of treatment is to burn away the offending wart with a caustic cream or liquid. Just the top of the wart should be covered with the caustic solution or compound. If this does not work, then do consult your doctor.

Splinters
Whether wood or metal, splinters should be removed as soon as possible. If they are deeply embedded in the flesh they should be removed by your doctor. If the splinter is sufficiently near the skin's surface for you to remove it yourself or for a friend or colleague to do it for you, then take the following precautions.

Wash the surrounding skin with warm water containing a little antiseptic and make sure you use clean cotton wool. The person who is removing the splinter should also wash his or her hands in plenty of hot water. Use a fine, sharp needle as a probe—but first sterilize it over a flame. When the splinter is removed make sure all the pieces are out, bathe the skin carefully, apply antiseptic ointment and cover with a clean dressing. Watch the wound for any indication that some foreign body is still present in the flesh—puffiness, excessive redness or 'weeping'—and see your doctor.

Rheumatics and arthritis
These complaints can be excruciatingly painful in old age—and they can sometimes stem from stiffness which was not treated earlier in life. Keep your hands supple and enjoy a balanced diet with a good quota of minerals and vitamins, to help keep your hands healthy for as long as possible. Remember that one of the joys of retirement is writing; another is reading. Without healthy hands both become very painful and difficult.

Industrial dermatitis
This is one of the commonest skin complaints which usually affects hands which come in contact with chemicals or modern manufacturing materials. If you do this type of manual work and notice any unusual soreness or rash marks do check this with your doctor, and give him full details of the equipment you are using at work. Watch out for the unusual at home, too: sudden contact with a new household product, such as a polish, washing powder or shampoo can easily cause an allergic rash to occur.

Allergies
Metal allergy is quite common—if you are given a beautiful new dress ring or bracelet and notice itching and soreness underneath it then it is quite possible that you have this allergy.

With a new baby, products come into the house which could cause problems: sterilizing solution for nappies [diapers] is usually strong stuff and combined with urine and metal from the pins, can cause unpleasant hand irritations for the young mother. Never immerse hands in these strong solutions.

No matter how busy you are, paying scrupulous attention to the care of your hands and taking precautions against infection will bring its own rewards. No matter what colour nail varnish you use, it will not hide the fact that your hands are not cared for. Remember that, apart from all the other tasks your hands perform, they are a means of expressing yourself. Well kept attractive hands will give great pleasure to others as well as yourself, and remember, it is never too late to care for your hands.

HAND LOOSENING

Exercise 1
Take the index finger of your left hand between the forefinger and thumb of your right, then shake your left hand vigorously. It should be completely limp. Repeat with the right hand.

Exercise 2
Imagine that you have just rinsed your hands in water. Now shake them vigorously to get rid of the water.

CO-ORDINATION
AND CONTROL

Exercise 1
Hold a pencil on the palm of your left hand with the palm of your right hand. Roll the pencil up and over the finger tips of your left hand and down the back to the wrist without dropping it.
Repeat three times.
Change hands and repeat.

WRIST STRENGTHENING

Exercise 1
Place the palms of your hands together, elbows apart as if you were about to pray. Now, pressing hands hard together, throw them forwards in a rapid jerky movement. Then bring them back to the vertical position again. Keep palms together throughout the movement. Repeat.

Exercise 2
With arms outstretched rotate wrists slowly in a clockwise movement, then repeat in the other direction.

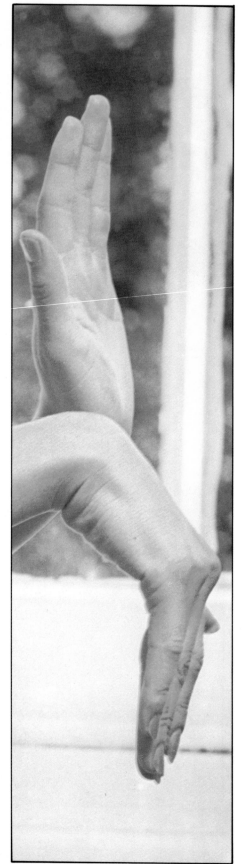

FINGER MOBILITY

Exercise 1
Hold a pencil between the thumb and first finger of your left hand. Now, without using your right hand twist the pencil between each finger, then back again. Repeat once, then repeat with your right hand.

Care for Your Nails

Good nails are essential to natural beauty. Cared-for-nails highlight attractive hands and feet. But dry, bitten or cracked nails can make them look dull and unattractive. Whether you are a housewife, a secretary, a businessman or a schoolgirl, your hands —and nails—play an important part in your activities. Because of this your nails need care. Just a few minutes attention every day, rather than leaving them to fend for themselves, can greatly improve them.

Nails are necessary because they protect the sensitive nerve endings in the tips of fingers and toes and aid blood circulation. Nails also act as a filter for acids and contain a tiny percentage of arsenic, which is a point to bear in mind if your nails accidentally scratch another person's face.

To understand how best to care for nails, it helps to know how a nail is formed and to remember that the nail is a delicate structure. The embryo nail is the soft, unformed nail lying at the base of the nailbed and behind the cuticle. The embryo nail consists of jel-like cells which, when they reach the air, become hardened, forming the nail-plate. These living cells then take their nourishment from the nailbed. But when they reach the free-edge, (the opaque margin at the fingertip end of the nailplate) they no longer attach themselves to the nailbed, and thus stop living.

The cuticle, the fold of skin at the base of the nailplate, protects the flesh in which the nail is embedded. The half-moon, often seen immediately above the cuticle, indicates the half-way stage between the embryo-jel formation and the finished, hardened nailplate. So, it is easy to see that these two areas in particular are very susceptible to damage.

The shape of your nail is determined by your bone structure. If your fingers are long and fine, your nails will follow a narrow shape, and similarly, if your bones are wide, your nails will be flatter and square-shaped. Many things can affect the growth of a nail, but on average, it takes about six months for a nail to grow from the embryo state to the free-edge, although it is generally faster in the summer, due to better blood circulation.

To keep the free edge of your nail in

good shape, you should shape it with the help of nail scissors, or clippers, and a file and emery board. Always buy the best quality. When buying a metal file, make sure it is an unplated, long file, measuring from six to eight inches and triple cut.

Your fingernails Clip each nail to give you approximately the right length. But do not cut shorter than the fingertip. Remember that this is what the nail is protecting. If the nail is clipped too short, the flesh becomes sensitive, bulgy and uncontrolled. The nail shouldn't be allowed to grow too long, as this can cause strain.

The nail file should be used to shape each nail into a gentle oval. The best way to ensure that you won't file away too much (particularly at the sides of the nail where nailplate should still be attached to nailbed) is to press your fingers on to a hard surface and the flesh will act as a natural barrier to stop you from going too far down. Don't file vigorously in a backwards and forwards movement. Instead, gently file in one direction with short, even strokes or from the sides to centre. Finish off with an emery board.

Your toenails Clip your toenails to the correct length, no shorter than the sensitive, fleshy tip of the toe. The toenail should be level with the toe itself and should be clipped straight across and not shaped at all. Use an emery board to smooth rough edges, not a steel file, and use light downward strokes.

Care of cuticles Acid from the nail generally makes the cuticle stick to the nailplate and this can cause two things to happen. Firstly, the cuticle is dragged up with the growing nailplate, until eventually it splits at the sides—a condition known as hangnail—which can lead to infection and soreness. And secondly,

should this happen, it will in turn affect the shape of the nail, making it uneven, smaller and flatter.

The most effective way to guard against this is to keep the cuticle completely free and clear of the nail. But how you do that is very important, when you remember how close the cuticle lies to the embryo nail, Never push the cuticle back with your fingers, a towel or any metal instrument, as you will damage the nail structure. When drying your hands with a towel, care should be taken to use a downward movement from the knuckles to the fingertips so that the cuticle is not disturbed in any way.

The correct way to keep cuticles free from the nailplate is to use a rubber-ended *hoof stick*. This gently lifts the cuticle away from the nailplate without pressing on the delicate structure below. It is also possible to use an orange stick wrapped in cotton wool, but it must be done with a rolling action and it takes longer. Once the cuticle is freed, it will shrink back of its own accord thus making cuticle removers or preparations unnecessary.

Nails and health Nails reflect your body health. Everything that happens to your body registers in your nails, which is why a doctor can often tell at a glance whether or not you've suffered recently from shock, a heart disorder, illness, diet deficiency or if you take drugs. Any of these troubles generally results in dry, flaky nails that break easily.

Diet is often the cause of bad nails and can be easily remedied by eating a good variety of foods. These should include protein, found in meat and fish, vitamins and minerals, found in fresh fruit and vegetables, calcium and fats, found in all the dairy foods like milk, butter, cheese, yogurt and eggs, and finally a small

amount of carbohydrate foods such as bread and cereals. Calcium and vitamins B, D and E are all vitally important for strong, healthy nails. Eating foods that you know still contain their original nourishment makes sense too. So choose plain, natural yogurt, brown wholemeal bread instead of white processed bread and brown sugar in preference to white, or better still, choose honey. Gelatine, too, is good for the nails, but buy the gelatine crystals from the chemists, not the grocer's packet cubes. One spoonful a day should see an improvement over six months.

Water is another reason why your nails may break. It doesn't matter whether it's hard, chalky drinking water, hard washing water, bath salts and long immersion in water, disinfectant in swimming pools, or bathing in the sea, water is the nail's worst enemy. Try drinking bottled spa water instead of ordinary tap water and use a water-softener when washing. Gloves should be used as often as possible, especially for jobs like washing-up and washing the car, as detergent, combined with the water, will strip the hands and nails of their natural oils. And don't shake talcum powder into gloves either, as this can cause irritation to the cuticles.

When you really can't avoid hands and nails coming into contact with water, be sure to use a handcream afterwards, to prevent the water drying out your nails. The best handcreams to use are those based on either animal fats (lanolin is sheep's fat), vegetable oils or nut oils. Mineral oils, liquid paraffin, glycerine and petroleum jelly aren't so good because they have no food value, and therefore cannot nourish the skin. The most quickly absorbed oil is almond oil. But with any handcream, it is the regularity with which it's used, rather than the amount and quality, that is the important factor.

Climate is another cause for flaking nails. A cold, damp climate spells disaster for nails. Poor circulation, plus hot and cold extremes of temperature on the blood stream, don't do nails much good, so remedy this by wearing warm, loose gloves, and by regularly massaging hands and fingers. Exercise, too, helps circulation. To aid circulation, open and close your hand repeatedly for several minutes and stretch your fingers as far as you can.

Occupational hazards Obviously, there are some people whose nails will be worse than average, because of what they do for a living. If you are a gardener, a builder, a potter, a baker, a hairdresser or a housewife, then you have to take more care of your nails, as sand, flour, clay, water and general wear and tear don't help the nails to grow strong. In particular, care must be taken to ensure that nails receive added nourishment. A good cream massaged into the fingertips every night should help, and, of course, plenty of handcream throughout the day.

If yours is the type of job where flour

20 Ways to Better Nails

1. Always use a handcream after washing your hands
2. Use a soft sponge to soap your nails clean
3. Use rubber gloves when doing jobs involving water
4. Wear gloves to protect your hands and nails against rough jobs like gardening
5. Use a pencil instead of your finger when dialling numbers on the phone
6. Use an emery board or metal file in one direction only
7. Give your feet and toenails regular massage and nourishing cream
8. Eat a well-balanced diet
9. Nourish your nails at night by using a hand lotion
10. Remember that hands and nails age first and fast, so look after them
11. Use the best quality nail files,

scissors and so on you can afford.
12. Never cut or file the corners of the nailplate away
13. Do not push the cuticle off the nailplate using your fingers, a towel or any sharp implement
14. Keep the free edge of your nails in good shape with the help of nail scissors or clippers
15. Your nails shouldn't be allowed to grow too long because this weakens them
16. Toenails shouldn't be shaped. Cut them straight across
17. Nail polish or fake nails shouldn't be used if your own nails are weak and brittle
18. Never bite your nails
19. If your nail problems appear serious, consult a doctor or manicurist
20. Don't expect faulty nails to be cured instantly. They'll take at least six months

or clay is likely to lodge beneath the free-edge, pay special attention to washing your hands and cleaning your nails. Don't use a nail brush or any sharp implement to prise dirt from underneath the nail. If you do, you'll only succeed in parting the nailplate from the nailbed, and you'll just have created a bit more surface in which the dirt can become embedded.

Use a nail brush on the palm of your hands and on the fingers. Do not use a brush on the backs of hands because of the veins. Clean the nails and fingertips with a sponge. Buy a natural cup-shaped sponge from any good chemist and soak it in warm, soapy water. Place the fingers and then the thumb in the sponge and squeeze gently so that the natural air-holes in the sponge will act as a suction and draw out the dirt. Then rinse your hands and dry them carefully. Apply a handcream and then, if you wish, buff your nails to a shine. The best buffer to buy is one with a chamois leather base, which should be moved in one direction only, across the nail, and not backwards and forwards, as this causes friction,

making the nailplate hot and the nails dry and brittle.

COMMON NAIL PROBLEMS

Breaking nails (*onychosis*) Broken nails are caused by water, wrong diet, or a diet lacking in calcium, shock, illness, nail infections, occupational wear and tear, cutting and filing away the sides of the nails, digging into the cuticles, rheumatism and acidity or allowing the nails to become too long.

Bad cuticles Split, dried or dragged cuticles are caused by acidity, rheumatism, wrong cutting, liquid acid cuticle removers, bad circulation, hot water, cuticles that have been wrongly pushed back, nail infections or occupational wear and tear.

Ridges Longitudinal ridges are often caused by rheumatism, acidity, bad circulation, accidental knocks or old age. Transverse ridges can be caused by illness, especially a high temperature, by digging into the cuticles, by shock or by accidental knocks.

Cuticle infection (*paronychia*) Infection of the cuticles can be caused by exterior

damage resulting from housework, gardening and from immersion in water, soap, soda, flour, sand and clay. Parasites, infection and some cuticle removers may also aggravate this problem.

Nail infection (*onychia*) The nails can be infected when the nailplate gradually separates from its bed. It looks like dirt, but is, in fact, discolouration due to a fungus and, if left unattended, may lead to *ringworm*.

White spots (*leukonychia*) White Spots are generally caused by external injury, such as nail biting, which separates the nail cells and allows air to get into the cells. Acid, collecting underneath the cuticle and growing up with the nail, can also produce white spots.

Some of these nail problems, such as transverse ridges, will correct themselves with time. But for others which are more serious, you should have a more specialized treatment. If you feel that your nails need professional treatment, see your doctor or a manicurist who will give you advice on the best kind of treatment to overcome specific problems which affect your nails.

Give Yourself a Manicure

Healthy, well-shaped nails make for an attractive appearance. You can reveal the natural beauty of your own nails by following this step-by-step guide to a do-it-yourself manicure.

The do-it-yourself manicure takes less than half an hour, costs you nothing and with a little care will leave your nails looking as if you'd been to a professional —although you'll have to put in all the effort. Don't worry about going wrong, just follow the instructions and you'll find nail care getting easier and easier.

The manicure is a full-scale beauty treatment for nails. Do it today and just a few minutes basic nail care as part of your normal grooming routine will keep your nails looking good for weeks. (Or, if you like, you can give yourself a regular manicure because you enjoy it.)

The first time you give yourself a manicure take things slowly—your nails are as delicate as other parts of your body. You'll need nail scissors, files and so on. But most of these you'll have already and the special implements—such as the *hoof stick*—are inexpensive.

Whether your nails are already good, or you're setting out to improve them, you'll find this manicure well worthwhile.

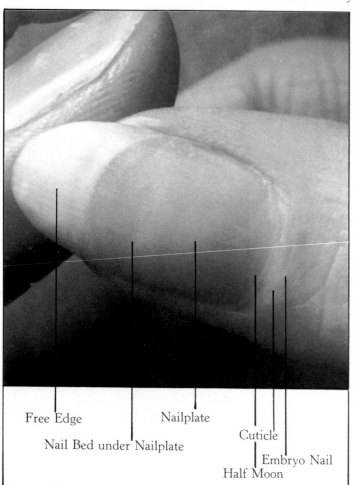

Free Edge
Nailplate
Nail Bed under Nailplate
Cuticle
Embryo Nail
Half Moon

What you will need to give yourself a manicure:
(a) triple-cut, steel file **(b)** handcream **(c)** soft sponge **(d)** soapy water **(e)** cotton wool **(f)** nail buffer **(g)** nail clippers **(h)** orange stick **(i)** cuticle trimmer **(j)** rubber-tipped *hoof stick* **(k)** emery board.

Follow this step-by-step treatment and give yourself a professional manicure. The numbers refer to the pictures on the opposite page. Carry out each step as carefully as you can.

1. Clean your nails using a soft sponge which has been dipped in warm, soapy water.
2. Clean the thumb separately to guarantee that it is given proper attention.
3. Clip each nail to the length you desire, using the centre of the clippers for the centre of the nail.
4. Use the curved edges of the clippers to clip the sides of the nail.
5. Do not clip too far down the side of each nail.
6. Use a triple-cut, steel file to smooth the edges of each nail into a good shape. File in one direction only, or from the sides to the centre of the nail.
7. To give an extra smoothness to the edges, use an emery board.
8. Soften the cuticles by applying soapy water with an orange stick. Cover its sharp end with cotton wool.
9. Use a cuticle trimmer to ease the cuticles gently upwards and away from the nailplate. Use a sideways, rolling action and be careful not to tear the cuticle.
10. Gently push the cuticle back using a rubber-tipped *hoof stick*. Use a sideways, twisting movement with the lightest touch possible.
11. Use a small pair of clippers to remove any tiny pieces of rough skin that might surround the nail.

But don't cut the cuticle.
12. Apply a nourishing cream to the cuticles, using an orange stick padded with cotton wool. Allow one minute for the cream to sink in. Then lightly rub any excess cream towards the fingertips.
13. Massage the fingers, using plenty of handcream, using a rotating movement to work towards the fingertips. Wipe away excess handcream with tissues.
14. Using an orange stick padded with cotton wool, gently clean under each nail to remove any remaining dirt.
15. Finally, buff each nail to a healthy shine, using the buffer in one direction only to prevent heat friction from drying the nails and causing them to crack.

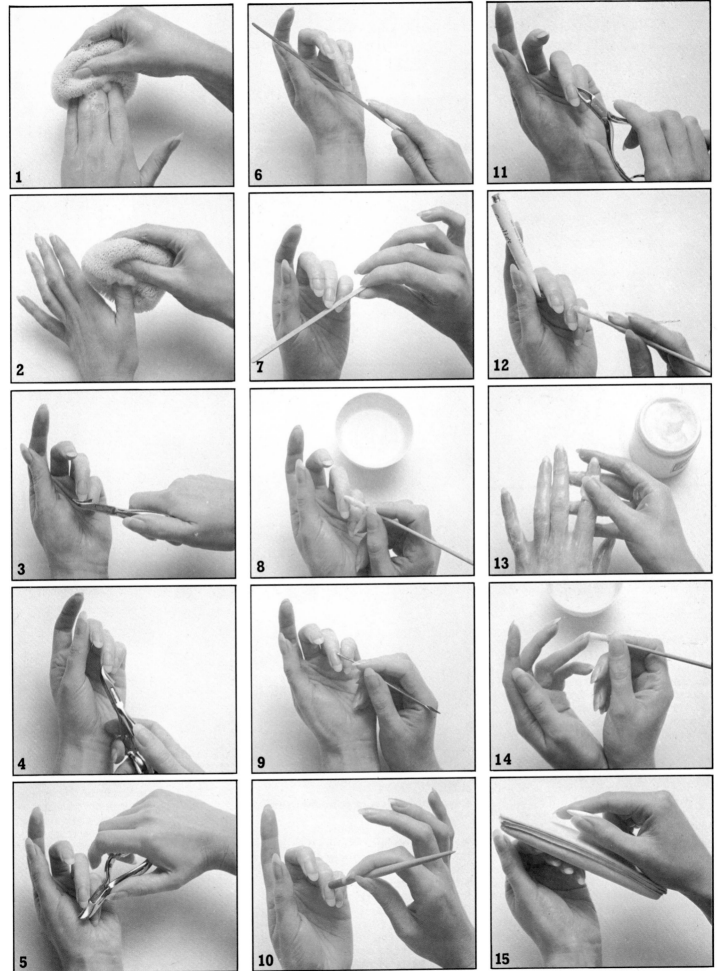

Exercises for the Back

The back is probably one of the most neglected and ill-used parts of the human body. Yet it can be one of the most beautiful. If you follow these exercises carefully your back will not only look good, it will feel good too. A long, lithe shape, freedom from tension and pain, a smooth, spot-free skin—these are the things to work for. A combination of exercise, massage and beauty care will help you achieve them.

Exercise can give you a supple back which is less likely to run to fat, and will also enable you to cope better with many tedious but necessary tasks in house or garden which involve stooping for long periods or lifting heavy weights. You cannot do exercises regularly but be lazy about posture all the rest of the time and still expect to gain full benefit from your exertions. Use the back exercises given here as a way of becoming aware of your back muscles and the way they behave and good posture should follow quite naturally. A fine, straight back and graceful carriage will win you compliments as well as making you feel fitter.

This simple routine of six exercises will help to trim away bulges and ease aches and pains at the same time. Follow the routine once a day, morning or evening, to improve both the look and feel of your back. Several of the exercises will also give relief when backache or tension strikes.

EXERCISE 1
Eases tension and relaxes the spine

A. Sit on the floor, back straight, legs apart at an angle of 45°, hands resting in front of you. Now bend your knees inwards, keeping your feet apart, and curl your body forward relaxing head and arms between your legs.
B. Slowly, raise your arms up and over your head until they are right behind you and place your hands, palms down, on the floor. Now take the weight of your body on your hands, arch your back very slowly and tip your head backwards. You should be able to feel the squeezing between the shoulderblades. The whole movement should be slow and controlled.
Repeat five or six times.

Breathing Breathe in to start exercise, out when your body is curled forwards, in again as you raise your arms.

EXERCISE 2
Tones upper back muscles, eases shoulder tension

Stand straight, with your feet slightly apart, arms by your sides. Now cross your arms behind your lower back. Give them a double bounce, swing hands and arms up and out sideways and cross them behind your head. Give a double bounce again, and swing them down. This movement should be done rapidly, with the arms well back. Repeat 20 times.

Breathing Breathe out after the first double bounce, in after the second (when your arms are crossed behind your head).

A

B

C

EXERCISE 3
Improves posture

A. Stand straight, with your feet slightly apart. Hold a narrow pole (a broom or mop handle will do). Your hands should be shoulder-width apart and your arms perfectly straight.
B. Raise the pole slowly up over your head.

C. Bring the pole down to the back of your neck, moving your arms but keeping your hands still. Do this slowly, so that you can really feel a strong pull just between your shoulderblades.
Repeat eight times.

Breathing Breathe in as you raise pole, out when it rests behind your neck.

EXERCISE 4
Firms the lower back muscles

A. Lie on your stomach on the floor, your hands beneath you, palms down, fingertips of both hands pointing towards each other. Now slowly raise your torso off the ground by straightening your arms and arching your spine. (This is similar to a classic yoga pose, which is known as the Cobra.)

B. Bend your left elbow slightly and twist around to look at your feet over your right shoulder. Straighten your left elbow, then repeat with the right elbow, twisting round to look at your feet over your left shoulder. Repeat five times to each side, then lower your body and relax for count of ten.

Breathing Breathe in as you raise your body and continue to breathe normally as you do the rest of the exercise.

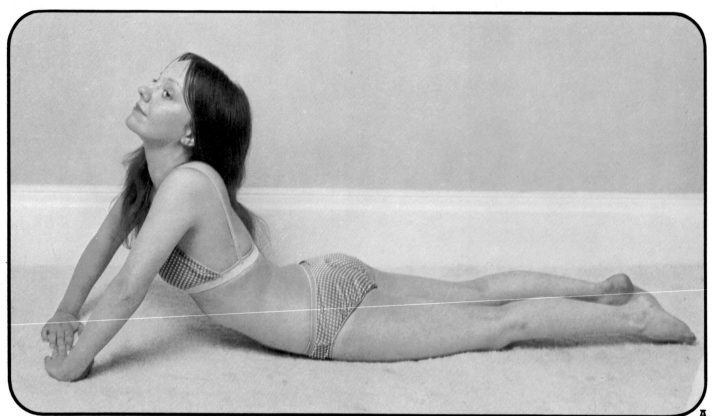

A

B

EXERCISE 5
Eases back strain and tension and improves posture

A. Sit on the floor with your back straight. Raise your right arm and bend the elbow so the hand touches the back of your head—keep the elbow well back. Now bend the left elbow and place your left hand, palm outwards, behind your waist.
B. Push your right hand further to the left until you can see your fingertips out of the corner of your left eye. At the same time push your left arm further to the right behind your waist. Do this twice, then relax and change hands.
Repeat 12 times.

Breathing Breathe normally throughout the exercise.

A

B

C

EXERCISE 6
Tones the back muscles generally

A. Stand with your feet apart, your left hand behind your head and the left elbow well out. Your right hand should be hanging comfortably by your side.
B. Keeping your feet firmly on the floor and your hips facing the front, twist the upper part of your body around to the right and touch the back of your left thigh with your right hand.
C. Swing to the front again, raising your right arm up to the side of your head as you do so.
D. Now twist the whole body round to the left and, keeping your spine perfectly straight, stretch well forward to touch your left foot with your right hand. If this seems easy, stretch your back just a bit more so

that you can touch the floor beyond your left foot. Return to the first position.
Repeat this five times, then change sides and repeat a further five times.

Breathing Breathe in at the start of the exercise, out as you touch the back of your thigh with your hand, in again as you raise your hand, and out as you finish the exercise.

Beauty Care for the Back

Until now we have been concerned chiefly with a group of exercises to tone up the muscles and firm the flesh. Exercise is one of the ways to achieve a beautiful back—but while working towards this, you should also pay scrupulous attention to cleansing and learn about the right cosmetic treatment for any skin troubles. Make-up can be very effective in improving on nature, particularly if your back is blemished, but it is not a substitute for really efficient and thorough cleansing.

This, the second part of the course, deals with cleansing and cosmetic care, and includes a relaxing back massage to help combat stress. Try this out with a friend or partner—and teach him or her the movements as you go, so that you can receive the soothing benefits of a back massage another time. Your back may be out of sight—but it should not be out of mind. Pay it some attention and look forward to increased suppleness and smoother, more attractive skin.

If you have ever juggled with two mirrors to try and catch a glimpse of your back view in a low-cut evening dress, you will know the worry that a sallow skin and a few spots can cause—it can even discourage you from wearing the dress of your choice. Unfortunately, the back is usually left out of regular beauty routines and when a bare back occasion does occur, neglect can show up in the most upsetting way.

Avoiding the mirror test altogether does not help—you may prefer to ignore the area between neck and waist if it is unattractive, but other people will not be able to. Because a person's vision is limited to the front and sides of her own body, it is easy to forget about the back view. If this applies to you, try glancing quickly over your shoulder into a mirror or any reflecting surface. What you see could be very different from your own mental image of how your back looks—yet when you bare your back that is the view that at least half the people you come into contact with see first. So the case for caring for your back is a strong one and like most beauty campaigns it begins in the bath.

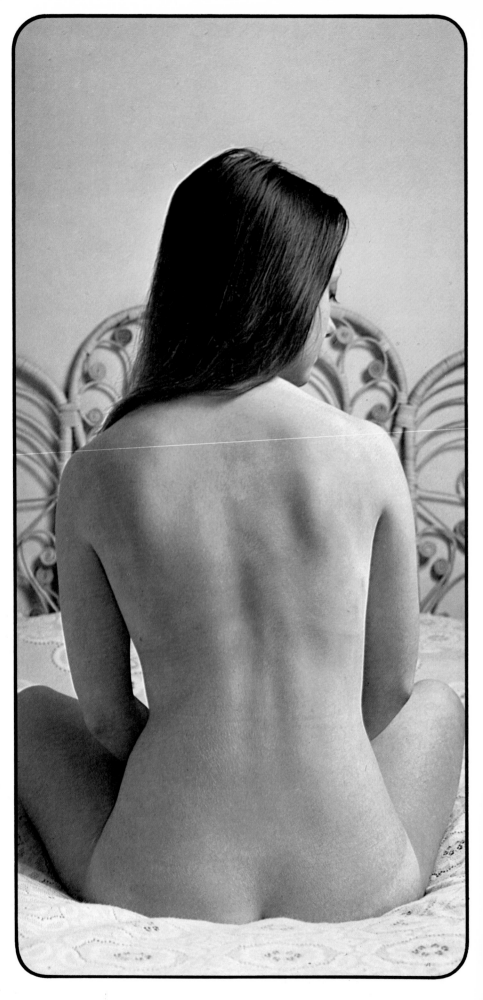

Bath-time routine

At least three times a week set aside some time while in the bath for a real back treatment.

The hollow between the shoulderblades is particularly prone to spots and sallowness and keeping the skin scrupulously clean is the first step to beating these problems. Perspiration often collects in this hollow and combines with the greasy sebum excreted by the sebaceous glands to produce fatty acids which can aggravate skin troubles such as blackheads and acne.

Use a soft bristle back-brush or a loofah. Avoid scratchy nylon brushes which could break the skin and irritate any existing spots and blemishes. Dry-scrub your back gently to stimulate circulation and get rid of dead skin. Next, using a mild, non-irritant soap and water, repeat the whole process for really thorough cleansing. Rinse by pouring water over your shoulders with a cup or basin. Then take a cool shower, concentrating the pressure of the water on your back. Turn it to cold if you can bear it.

When you get out of the bath, dry your back carefully with a soft fluffy towel. If there are any painful blemishes, just pat the skin dry, do not rub. The best way to make sure that the towel reaches every part of your back is to hold one end of the towel in your right hand, let the towel hang over your right shoulder and then take the bottom of it in your left hand. There is no need to scrub the flesh in a rough sawing motion, move the towel very gently.

If the skin on your shoulders and back is greasy, splash it with an astringent skin tonic, rubbing with oily bath lotion will only make things worse. If the skin is dry, however, lavish a little face nourishing cream on your back from time to time and use bath lotion in between. Talcum powder is not a good idea. It tends to dry up an over-dry skin still more, and it combines with grease and perspiration to add to oily skin troubles.

Blemishes

The first essential for dealing with a poor skin condition is to keep the skin scrupulously clean. But there are lots of other things to do to overcome the problem.

Hair

Long hair for example, although it does not cause the trouble, can aggravate back blemishes. When the sebaceous glands produce too much grease the surplus is trapped in the back hollow. (This can be triggered off, particularly at puberty, by emotional or hormone action or a combination of both.) Greasy hair touching the back adds even more oil—even clean hair has a slightly greasy protective coating. So, if you have acne or bad spots on your back it should help to keep your hair clear of your back and shoulders, keeping it clean at all times.

Clothing

Warm clothing can make the hollow between the shoulder blades—where spot-inducing grease and dirt are trapped —even more receptive to blemishes. It is important to allow perspiration to escape —so cotton or smooth woollen clothing is best. Synthetic fabrics like nylon are non-porous and not recommended. The best way to combat the build-up of perspiration and keep the skin cool is to wear a cotton vest under top clothes winter and summer. Alternatively, a cotton T-shirt worn on its own in summer or under a sweater in winter will do the same efficient job. Dressing in layers is also a good idea if you want to keep cool—even in winter, centrally-heated offices are usually warm enough to work in shirt-sleeves, or a light blouse. It is pointless to spend all day perspiring in over-heated rooms.

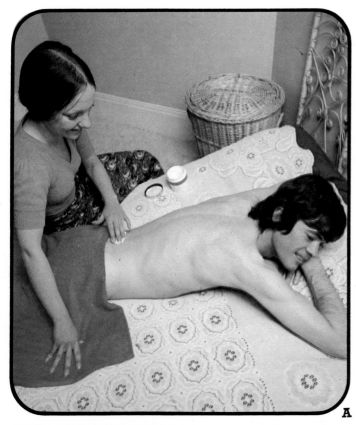

A

B

ANTI-STRESS MASSAGE

Shoulders, back and neck muscles are very vulnerable to stress. For the harrassed worker a soothing back massage at the end of a busy day can be effective in reducing tension, which is in itself the cause of many nagging troubles–poor

digestion, sleeplessness, irritability, general fatigue.

Try giving a friend or partner a massage to relax back and shoulders. Remember that your hands should be gentle but firm. Your hands may ache after the first time, but will soon gain strength.

Your partner should lie comfortably on a firm mattress or table, over which a towel may be laid. His or her elbows should be bent with hands underneath the forehead, palms downwards.
A. Place a hot towel on your partner's back for a few moments

Food

A good diet is as important for a clear skin on your back as it is for a beautiful facial complexion. Eating chocolate and fried foods will not alone make your back spotty but it will leave less room for the vitamin and mineral-providing foods which will actually help clear up skin troubles.

Food is the fundamental fuel for the efficiency of every part of the body, including skin health. Eat fresh fruit instead of chocolate, salads instead of fried foods, green vegetables instead of starchy pastries. Try to drink water sometimes in place of cups of tea or coffee. Make a point of drinking half a pint of milk a day and eat yogurt as a tasty snack or dessert.

Skin care

Treat a spot-blemished back in exactly the same way as you would treat your face. Fortunately, you are not likely to irritate spots and blackheads on your back by squeezing them since they are too difficult to reach. Concentrate on deep-cleansing (with the bath-time treatment) and toning with skin-tonic. Use a germicidal cream on badly-infected spots, but avoid creams which dry out the top layer of the skin.

A weekly sauna bath will deep-cleanse the pores, and the dry heat is more comfortable than the humid atmosphere of a Turkish bath. And if you swim in a public pool, be sure to take a shower afterwards. Dirt and chemicals in the water could aggravate any skin condition. Sea-bathing is excellent as the salt is soothing—but do shower as soon as possible afterwards as dry salt makes the top layer of skin over-dry. Sun-bathing will help dry up surface grease, but usually the effect is only temporary. Before a special bare back occasion a course of ultra-violet treatment can be a useful measure. Three or four very short treatments will give a faintly golden appearance to the skin and any blemishes will be less obvious. An overnight 'instant' tan will achieve the same effect.

Disguise

Freckles, birth marks and scars can be camouflaged with clever make-up, but you need two good mirrors and a steady hand to do the job without assistance. It is far better to get a friend to help if you can. To look good, back make-up must be lightly applied, and it must not come off when touched. Liquid or grease-based make-ups are unsuitable as they may run and streak when you get hot—

and will certainly come off on the hand of a dancing partner, or on your evening dress.

First, cover blemishes and spots with a medicated covering cream which exactly matches your skin tone. If you are on your own, do this with a long-handled brush, using only a very little cream at a time. Work sitting down, with your back to a large mirror, holding a smaller mirror in your left hand to check your progress. Apply cake make-up with a damp sponge all over your back. (Choose a tone which is slightly darker than the skin tone if you want to help freckles to blend in.) Be sure that the make-up is taken right down below dress-level, and brought around to the sides of your body and over shoulders too. Theatrical cake make-up is good for this as it lasts even in a warm atmosphere, being designed to stay matt under hot lights. Finish with a light dusting of translucent pressed face powder to give a pearly glow.

You can protect the inside of your evening dress from the make-up by stitching a strip of thin fabric just inside the neckline. Check your back view every hour or so during the evening, and touch up with translucent powder if necessary.

 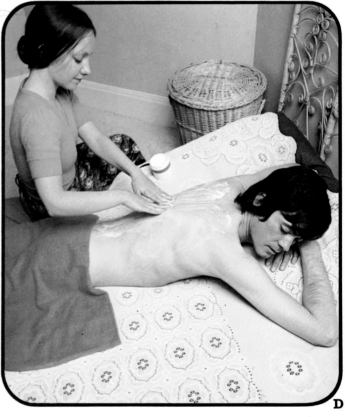

to open the pores, then put a few drops of massage oil (patchouli fragrance is particularly relaxing) or dabs of massage cream at the base of the spine. Remember that the massage movements you are going to make should be slow and graceful—the smoother the

pressure, the more relaxing it is.
B. Spread your fingers and place your hands at the base of your partner's spine.
C. Move your fingers slowly up the back, one on each side of the backbone, and then over the shoulders.

Repeat this movement about 20 times.
D. Lightly press the tips of your fingers up and down on your partner's shoulders, then drag your hands firmly down each side of the spine to waist level.
Repeat eight times.

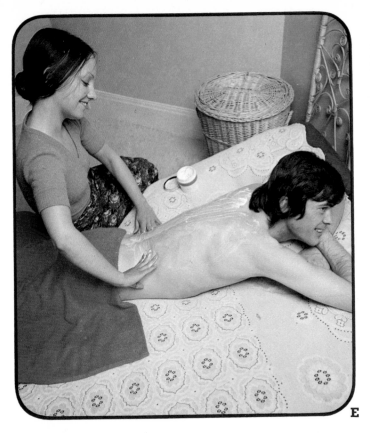

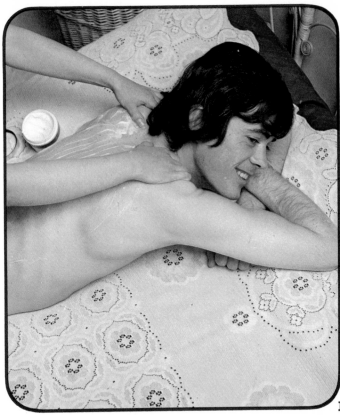

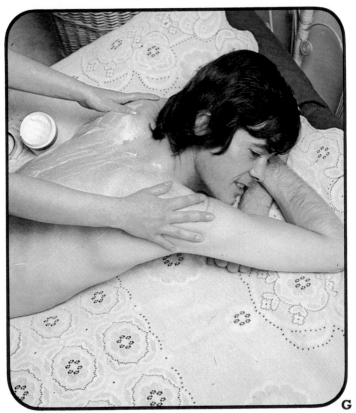

E. Now place your hands on each side of the backbone at waist level, spread the fingers and bring your hands outwards and down to the side of the waist.
Repeat 10 times.
F. Place your hands lightly one on each shoulder and, using only the thumbs, make small circles on each side of the back of the neck. This should be done very gently.
G. Now spread your fingers and make big circles on the shoulders, working steadily outwards.
H. Finally, move your hands firmly down from the shoulders to the base of the spine.
Repeat 20 times.

Let your partner or friend relax in the same position for about 10 minutes after the massage, then wipe off any residue of oil with a paper tissue. After a massage, a shower is very invigorating, and it also helps remove the greasiness of the oil or cream which is used in the massage.

Breast Care

Is your mental picture of the ideal bosom one of small, firm breasts, or of sumptuous curves? Whatever the ideal breast size, the essence of a beautiful bosom is firm, healthy breasts. Even if you are not entirely happy with the appearance of your breasts, don't feel that nothing can be done and so neglect them entirely. Regular care can improve the shape and general appearance of your breasts. A little time and attention can go a long way towards making them healthier and more attractive.

Modern science is on the side of women. There is a vast selection of bras made out of cool, stretchable fabrics, which are designed to fit comfortably and flatter any shape. Add to this the advances made in the field of cosmetic surgery and you will find the future is not as black as you thought. At times in the past, women regarded breasts more as a fashionable asset than as an attractive part of their bodies. Now, with the return of more natural figures, it is essential to make the most of whatever size breasts you have and concentrate on keeping them firm and shapely.

Because the breasts are basically made up of cells, gland tissues, milk ducts, fibrous tissues and fat rather than muscles, they benefit from three things —good posture, support and regular exercise.

Posture

Trying to minimize large breasts by hunching the shoulders forward only succeeds in drawing attention to them and making the body fall into an unnatural, ugly shape. Instead, get into the habit of standing well. Keep your back straight and shoulders back, stomach and buttocks held in. Look straight ahead at eye level so that your head is evenly poised above the spine and your chin is at right angles to your neck. Although this will not make a large bosom look smaller, it will make you look taller and slimmer and give you a better overall shape.

Being aware of your body shape means that good posture is an integral part of all your movements. So, having found the correct standing position, make sure you walk with most of your weight on the forward leg.

Always bend from the waist, standing with your legs slightly apart so that your weight is evenly distributed. When you lift something heavy from the floor approach it squarely stooping so that the whole body takes the weight, not just the back. When carrying a heavy object, keep

your body upright and let the arm and shoulder take the weight.

Sit down by keeping the top half of your body straight and lowering yourself slowly into the chair. Once sitting, keep your back straight, stomach in and trunk pushed deep into the chair. Reaching upwards should be a movement of the whole body, keeping your back straight and weight evenly balanced on the balls of the feet.

Remember to keep all movements relaxed and flowing, not stiff and jerky. Bad posture can ruin even the best bustline. Make an effort to correct any tendency to slump. This will produce an improvement immediately, since the breasts will be lifted up and away from the rib cage.

Support

Because breasts have no muscles of their own, and are only supported by the pectoral muscles, extra support is needed for busts of all sizes, and a bra should be worn as soon as the breasts start developing at puberty. Going without a bra now and again, if your breasts are small, firm and young, will do no harm. It might, however, be unwise to make a habit of it because some doctors believe it can lead to sagging breasts later in life. Obviously, the smaller and lighter the breasts the less likely they are to sag, and the larger the breasts the more the need for extra support.

To know what sort of size category your breast comes into, first measure the fullest part of your breasts. Take the measure from your back round and over the nipples at the front. Now measure just under the breasts. The difference between the two measurements will give you a rough guide as to whether you should look for a small, medium or large bra cup. A four- to five-inch difference would probably need an A or B bra cup; a five- to six-inch difference, a B or C cup, and seven inches or over suggests heavy breasts which would need a C or D cup. The main thing to remember when buying a bra is to take your time and give yourself plenty of choice. If possible get an experienced fitter to help you.

A well-fitting bra should have the back piece and sides level with the front. Most of the support should come from beneath the breasts. (Check this by slipping the straps down to see if the bra will stay in place without them.) If the back piece tends to be high around the shoulder-blades this could mean either that you are hauling your breasts up by the shoulder straps, or that the base of the bra does not fit. Bulging flesh at the back of the bra or at sides and underarms means the bra is too small. And if the fabric cuts into the flesh at the front, the cups are too small. If the cups are creased all over or if the bra does not move with you, the cups are probably too big.

When trying on new bras, settle the breasts gently into the cups with your hands, leaning forward at the same time. Never force them into an obviously unnatural bra shape just because it makes your cleavage look good. There are specially-designed bras for this which involve no discomfort.

When choosing a bra for heavy breasts, make sure that it has flat, well-padded under-cup wiring that will fit comfortably against the rib cage, not against the breasts, and wide elasticized straps that give support to the centres of the breasts. Small breasts can be enhanced with the help of lightly-padded bras and under-wiring, but it is essential to keep the bustline natural and not to throw the rest of the body out of proportion. Many women have one breast smaller than the other. If this difference is obvious choose the cup size of your bra to fit the larger breast and pad the other cup very slightly with soft, absorbent material.

Be prepared for your breasts to change size and buy different bras accordingly. The breasts continue to grow up to the age of about 22. And either pregnancy or the contraceptive pill can often cause quite large increases, due to changes in the hormone balance, although these may be only temporary. Busts that become over-large in pregnancy may tend to sag after the birth, although women who breast-feed often regain their original size more quickly. Pregnant women should give careful thought to what they eat and be sure always to wear bras that really support their breasts.

Very large or very small breasts can at times bring about psychological complexes. Most women can overcome such problems by clever choice of bras and

clothes. For those who are really unhappy, plastic surgery can increase or decrease bust size and the methods are improving all the time. Cosmetic surgery is expensive, although in some countries such operations are available through health schemes if a patient can prove to her doctor that the size of her breasts is causing constant misery and discomfort. Large breasts are reduced by removing some of the excess from the area below the nipples. A small breast is enlarged with the introduction of implants. Both operations leave scars and the breasts need a lot of extra care for several weeks afterwards.

Care

Your daily bath or all-over wash should include gently washing the breast area in order to remove accumulated perspiration. In hot weather, heavy breasts benefit from a cotton bra, and constant use of talcum powder will help to keep them dry. After washing, splash the breasts with cold water to help firm the tissue. Follow this by a gentle fingertip massage (using the pads of the fingers), to smooth in a nourishing cream. If you discover any lumps or swellings in the breasts consult your doctor immediately. The chances are that it will be nothing serious—some slight swelling is normal immediately before a menstrual period —but the fact remains that the breast area is one of the most cancer-prone parts of a woman's body.

If hairs around the nipples worry you, try either plucking them out, or have them removed professionally by electrolysis. This can be done at a beauty salon. Both methods are perfectly safe although the latter tends to be the more effective and long-lasting.

Clothes

Careful choice of clothes is all-important in under-playing a large bust or defining a small one. If your breasts are large try to lead the eye away from the bust by selecting dresses with sleeve interest or by wearing a striking belt. Empire-line dresses gathered under the bust are particularly unflattering to women with large bosoms. Never wear jersey or other clinging material in bright, shiny colours —these will only emphasize unwanted curves. And avoid fabrics with horizontal or diagonal stripes. To make a large bust appear smaller choose plain, dark, matte fabrics. Balance up your figure by wearing flared or gored skirts. Both full-length and knee-length skirts can look good, but never wear them really short.

Women with small breasts need clothes which are cleverly darted to give the illusion of fullness. Pale, shiny fabrics have an enlarging effect, too, and close-fitting, well-tailored clothes will help.

Always remember that, however smart your clothes, there is no substitute for daily care of the breasts and a really well-fitting bra.

POINTS TO REMEMBER
1 Choose a bra that gives uplift and cleavage in order to make the most of small breasts.
2 It is sensible to wear a bra, particularly if you have heavy breasts.
3 Exercise regularly in order to keep breasts firm.
4 Walk tall and be proud of your breasts—whatever their size.
5 Only consider plastic surgery as a last resort—it is expensive.
6 Do not be deceived by numerous products on the market which claim to be 'miracle' bust improvers— there is no proof that they work.
7 Do keep your shoulders back and be conscious of your posture at all times.
8 Do not scorn padded bras. They can give a better shape.
9 Do wear a swimsuit with a built-in bra.
10 Always consult your doctor about any breast problems.

Exercises for the Breasts

To help tone up and strengthen the pectoral muscles—the muscles which support the breasts—and to improve general posture, exercise must be done regularly. This will lift breasts and firm them and so improve both small and large breasts. Because each individual differs, it may be that a small-breasted person will actually add inches to her bustline, whereas another might only improve her overall shape.

Large breasts can be reduced by a combination of diet and exercise. By cutting down on fried foods, fats and carbohydrates your body will be forced to draw on stored fats, some of which are in the breasts. Exercise will not actually reduce the size of the breasts but because it firms them it will give you a better, more youthful bustline.

Exercising also prevents breasts from drooping. Breathing deeply from the diaphragm, without raising the shoulders, is perhaps the easiest exercise aimed at strengthening the pectoral muscles, but both swimming and skipping are also great bust improvers.

Swimming, using both the breast stroke and the back stroke, is particularly beneficial because the water resistance strengthens the effectiveness of the exercise, and the water makes you weightless for a while—relieving the continual pull of gravity on the breasts. Swimsuits with built-in support cups are best if your breasts tend to be heavy.

When skipping, use a long rope (about four yards of ordinary thin rope) to ensure that the arms are lifted and fully extended with the skipping movement. It is best to do slow backwards skips as these lift the bust.

The following routine is designed to firm the breasts by strengthening the pectoral and shoulder muscles. Do the exercises energetically, but relax between each one. The whole routine can be done in 15 minutes, so you should easily be able to fit it in once a day. The results will not be dramatic, but your breasts will undoubtedly look and feel firmer and they will be less likely to sag in later years.

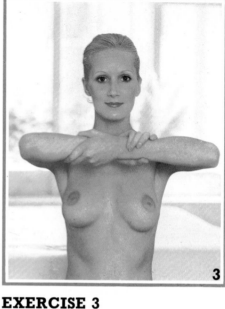

EXERCISE 3
Stand with feet slightly apart and arms folded at shoulder height. Grip your forearms tightly with your hands just above wrists. Now push your elbows towards each other in short, hard jerks. Relax. Repeat five times.

EXERCISE 1
Kneel on the floor or stand upright with feet slightly apart, arms at the side of the body. Now swing your arms up, over and back. Then, without moving your shoulders, let your arms relax.
Repeat 10 times.

EXERCISE 2
Bring your arms up over your head and swing them behind your back as far as possible—arching your back and dropping your head back. Lock hands together at waist level. Hold for a count of five.
Repeat 10 times.

EXERCISE 4
Hold your arms straight out in front of you at shoulder height. Pull your hands slowly towards your shoulders bending your arms and clenching your hands as though pulling something towards you. Repeat five times.

EXERCISE 5
Lie on your stomach on the floor
with elbows bent, and fingertips
facing inwards under the shoulders.
Rest your forehead on the floor.
Slowly raise your head and push
down with hands, raising your
body, arching your spine and
bending your neck backwards.
Finally, pull in the stomach muscles
and lift your stomach off the floor.
Slowly lower upper back and
shoulders to floor and return to
original position, breathing deeply
and slowly. Now relax.
Repeat three times, building up to
five.

EXERCISE 6
Stand up straight with your back
pressed firmly against a wall,
heels two to three inches away
from the wall. Raise your hands
above your head and push them
flat against the wall, palms facing
outwards. Push chest forward,
arching your back. Repeat five
times.

EXERCISE 7

Stand with feet slightly apart and
raise your arms to shoulder level.
Now place your left fingers on left
shoulder and right fingers on right
shoulder and rotate your elbows in
an anti-clockwise direction.
Rotate 10 times.

EXERCISE 8

Stand with legs slightly apart and
raise your arms to shoulder level
so that your elbows are bent and
hands are clasping about eight
inches in front of you. Place palms
together, as if praying, and take a
deep breath pressing the heels of
your hands together as hard as you
can. Hold for a count of five,
breathing out. Now relax.
Repeat five times.

EXERCISE 9

Stand about two feet away from a
wall, with your heels together.
Breathe in deeply and rock forward,
placing the palms of your hands
horizontally on the wall, fingers in
line with shoulders, elbows bent.
Breathe out slowly, pushing heels
of hands into wall to a slow count of
five. Return to upright position and
relax arms. Repeat five times.

How to Keep Your Bottom Beautiful

A trim and well-rounded bottom is an essential feature of a good figure. Although it is the part of the body that you yourself view the least, it is a feature that other people are able to view more often. There is much you can do to keep it in trim.

The buttocks are the fleshy cushion-like covering, intended to protect the rear of the 'hip girdle'. Buttocks vary greatly from person to person, but they are, to a greater or lesser extent, soft and rounded. They provide a perfect natural seat.

The hip girdle itself consists of three pairs of strong, flattish bones which together form a shallow 'basin' In adults

It is important that your bottom looks good and keeping it in shape is the best way to ensure this.

these bones are firmly and strongly set, while in children they are quite loose. They usually become fully strengthened by the time the child is 14 years old. The hip girdle is connected to the spine and to the legs. In women the hip and entire buttock area are slightly wider and shorter than in men. A woman's hip girdle and buttocks encase her reproductive organs and womb where the foetus must have enough room to grow.

This does not mean, however, that a woman's buttocks need be excessively fleshy. The shape to aim for is firm and gently rounded, broadening slightly as the buttocks reach the top of the thighs.

The muscles in the buttocks extend throughout the seat. Their function is to pull the thighs sideways and backwards and to raise the trunk from a stooping position.

There is no doubt that the bottom is a very functional part of the body. It does an essential job. It is also a difficult part of the anatomy to keep looking neat and in good shape. This is particularly true in women. On the whole, women spend more time sitting down than men. Of the female working population a greater proportion is in sedentary occupations than in the male working population. Most housewives spend a great deal of their working day sitting.

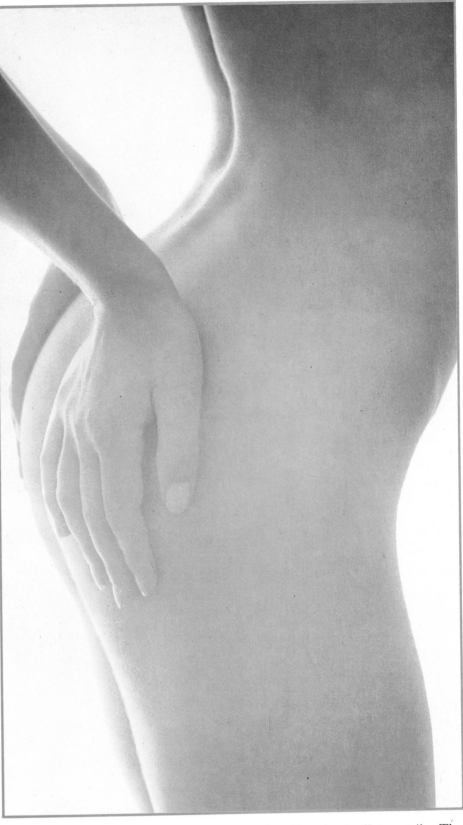

Although buttocks were designed to be sat on, they were never meant to be put to this use for most of the time. Another point to bear in mind is that the back of the body is rarely looked after quite as carefully as the front. When problems are not seen, their existence tends to be ignored.

There are certain rules you can follow if you want to have a shapely and beautiful bottom. Remember that while you may not see the problem, other people will notice it all too easily. The routines for a beautiful bottom are not difficult to learn, or to carry out.

Probably, the most admirable of rear views belong to infants. A baby's bottom has soft, smooth skin which matches the rest of his body in colour and texture. As the human body matures, however, the skin on the buttocks often becomes coarser. The colour of the skin, too, can change. It can become greyish because clothing has stopped the air from reaching the skin or from restricted circulation.

It is not being suggested that it is necessary to become a nudist to have a beautiful bottom. On the other hand, there are some very useful basic rules to follow and the effects will be noticed both in and out of clothes. The first of these is not to wear tight underwear if your bottom is at all inclined to be spotty. This is a very common problem with men. The problem is made worse for men who do a lot of driving. They often find that their buttocks become covered in spots.

Nylon pants make matters worse still. They prevent the inevitable build-up of perspiration from escaping properly. Close contact with hot leather or plastic car seat covers over long periods means that perspiration is trapped in a kind of vacuum and cannot evaporate properly. This encourages spots to develop.

One way of reducing the risk of getting spots in this way is to wear underwear made of fine cotton. Trousers made in natural fibres such as wool and cotton mixture are preferable. Natural fibres are cooler than man-made materials and give more ventilation. It is also advisable not to drive continuously for long periods, but to take regular breaks. Several hygiene precautions can be taken to guard against this condition. It is important to bathe daily. This should be followed with a liberal dusting with an anti-perspirant dry-spray talc.

If you wear tight jeans or trousers, make sure your bottom is a neat shape and not contorted by the clothes you wear. If flesh is restricted too tightly it may become rough in texture and greyish in colour. These two conditions occur because of restricted circulation in the skin tissues. If you like wearing tight trousers, give your buttocks a circulation tone-up each night with a dry bath glove before having a bath. Try to improve muscle tone as well. Apart from wearing the proper clothing, regular beauty care at bathtime will help keep the bottom soft and smooth.

The first thing to do is to check your rear view using two mirrors. Look for a coarse skin texture, poor muscle tone and a reddish or greyish skin. You may notice some curious silvery 'threads' on either side of the bottom. These may be due to the effects of puberty. A woman's shape changes dramatically during this period of development. These threads are stretch marks and can also appear when weight is either lost or put on very quickly.

It is possible to damage the tissues under the skin as a result of wearing a tight stretchy girdle. Fortunately, these garments are now seldom worn by young women, so the possibility of damage is reduced. This is still, however, a common problem in older women. It is always best to rely on the natural firmness of the muscles, or muscle tone, to hold the bottom in, rather than rely on synthetic stretch fibres to do the job for you.

When taking a bath pinch large hand-

Driving a car regularly and for long periods is very tiring. In time, your bottom will become flabby unless some precautions are taken. To keep your beautiful bottom the following exercises can be done— when the car is parked.

EXERCISE 1

Grasp the steering wheel at the '9 o'clock' and '3 o'clock' hand positions. Press back hard with your buttocks into the angle of the seat. Contract the buttock muscles. As you do this, press back against the seat with your heels. You should feel the muscles working hard under your upper thighs. Hold this contraction for a count of six. Repeat as often as you can without tiring.

EXERCISE 2

This is a breathing exercise. Sit upright in your seat, clasp your hands around your knees. Contract your buttock muscles as you inhale. As you exhale bring your shoulders forward raise your bottom from the car seat. Repeat several times.

fuls of flesh on your buttocks. This should be done when your entire body is under the water. It is a good idea to put a generous amount of bath oil into the water. This will be a great help in softening your skin. The pinching process will not be painful and will help break down the fatty tissues and encourage efficient circulation.

Once you have finished bathing, apply a generous amount of body lotion to your buttocks. If they are rather on the spotty side, dry yourself carefully and re-wash the spotty areas with a medicated liquid soap. Make sure that the skin is completely dry before putting on underwear. If you suffer from excessive perspiration in this area choose cotton pants in preference to nylon.

A good tip is to apply facial moisturizing cream on very dry and flaky areas. The skin on the buttocks is very sensitive. It is as sensitive as the face and needs gentle handling and care. Try to do as much walking as possible to exercise the muscles in the buttocks.

There are some simple everyday hazards which can detract from a bottom's good shape. One of these is the apparently innocent soft cushion. If you are in a job that requires you to sit down virtually all the time, make sure that the chair you sit on is firm. On a soft surface the fleshy

parts of the buttock will sag. There will be no resisting force for the muscles to work against. In time, they will simply become flabby from disuse. Since women usually have more flesh on their buttocks than men, this is a predominantly female problem.

A man is unlikely to develop a large spreading bottom until much later in life, even if he is a sedentary office worker. His buttocks will rarely become larger until middle age when body flesh generally begins to thicken. A simple precaution against a flabby bottom is to sit on a firm seat which also gives adequate back support.

Trousers made in rough materials may cause irritation to the skin on the buttocks. Beware of very hairy fabrics such as knobbly tweeds, rough serge or mohair. These may chafe against delicate skin. If necessary, choose rough textured trousers but with a smooth lining to avoid this problem. A smooth wool or wool and cotton mixture is most suitable against the scant protection provided by modern underwear.

Excessive suntanning can cause soreness and burning. By wearing trunks or a bikini brief reaching almost to the waist one day, then wearing a very brief pair of pants the next, you can help to eliminate discomfort. Any area of skin which has not been exposed to the sun for a long time is extremely vulnerable. It is best to tan your lower back slowly, with only a few minutes' exposure the first day then gradually build up to longer periods. You could invest in a proper all-over sun tanning course at a local health club. There, at least, a tan can be achieved painlessly.

Sports such as riding, cycling and motor cycling can cause quite severe soreness and chafing on the bottom and the back of the upper thighs. The best way to deal with this condition is to rub in some linament which will reduce pain considerably. Follow this with a hot bath. Add a cupful of vinegar to the water to help relieve aches and pains as well as smooth the skin and ease soreness or stiffness. Try to regulate sporting activity wisely instead of becoming exhausted the first time out. Muscles which are not accustomed to hard work need gradual initiation. While riding, for example, the buttock muscles are vibrated or bumped up and down. They are also heavily used while the rider maintains control of the horse. Once you are aware of the effects of hard labour on your bottom, you can take the necessary care to keep your bottom protected.

A good-looking and well-shaped bottom is an indispensible feature of a good figure. You can attain the desirable shape and size by following your beauty care with an exercise routine. Take good care of your bottom. A bottom that is both attractive and in proportion will do a great deal for your self-confidence. You will feel good because other people think you look good.

Most people do far more sitting down than is good for them, or their bottoms. It is also true that many of the chairs we use are very bad for posture. They are either too soft or the wrong shape. The bottom is a very good natural seat. We carry our own cushion of flesh around with us. Even the thinnest person carries enough padding around to support the weight of the upper part of the body. Because of this, additional soft upholstery to sit on should not really be necessary. Worse than this, a seat that is too soft is actually harmful to the development of good muscle control.

For a woman, the most common fault is likely to be a large, sagging or flabby bottom. There are a number of useful excercises you can practise to help correct this fault.

Good stance is essential to beauty and grace. There is no point in possessing the most attractive figure in the world if you habitually slouch. The whole effect will be ruined. Poor stance could cause flab to form over the buttocks as the muscles weaken due to incorrect use. The following routine to correct poor stance could prove very useful indeed.

Stand with your hips held evenly, both on the same level. Your body should be perfectly straight and stretched upwards.

Now, tuck your bottom in, contracting the muscles slightly as you do so. To start off with, you will have to think about doing this. As time goes on, however, it will gradually become an unconscious reflex action and one that will help greatly in improving your figure and stance.

Equally important you should try to improve walking posture. A slouching and shambling gait can greatly detract from your appearance and, in time, the shape of your bottom will suffer. As in the routine to improve stance, the first thing to do is to keep the hips firm and

---

The correct exercises will help keep your bottom in trim, which is essential for a good figure.

---

on the same level. If you wriggle your hips a great deal when you walk, there is a danger that the joints between the spine and the hip girdle will become loose. If this happens it will result in strained muscles and possibly even arthritis later on. A wobbly walk will also make a large bottom look even larger simply by drawing attention to it.

To correct a wobbly walk, keep your shoulders back and your bottom and stomach well in. Contract your buttock muscles while you are walking.

From time to time, study your walking posture in shop windows as you walk along. Check whether your bottom is tucked in properly. If it is not, correct your walking posture accordingly.

Bottoms vary enormously from person to person and a woman's bottom is a very different shape from a man's, being wider and more fleshy. As far as the female bottom is concerned, there are a number of very common shape problems.

One of these is the 'sagging' bottom. All bottoms have more flesh at the lower end of the buttocks, where they meet the thighs, than they have nearer the spine. This flesh may look loose and even hang in folds. It is possible to have a 'tuck' taken in this loose flesh by means of cosmetic surgery. A great improvement, however, can be made by taking regular exercise. This is particularly true if the sufferer is still quite young. The wearing of a panti-girdle may make the condition itself worse. Muscles which are encased and not used will, in time, become sluggish.

Another quite common shape problem is a condition known as 'jodphur' bottom. It is so called because the sufferer has unsightly protruberances of excess flesh at hip level. Her silhouette almost gives the impression that she is wearing jodphurs. To disperse this flesh, regular and deep massage can help, but proper exercise is also necessary. A dramatic improvement is often noted after a course of muscle-toning treatment, but the problem will reappear if bad sitting and posture habits are continued.

The problem of the 'wobbling' bottom is very common and can be quite embarrassing for a woman. Because of this, it is tempting to wear a girdle. However, this will increase the slackness of the buttock muscles instead of building muscle tone. If the problem is accompanied by a general surplus of flesh, as it usually is, then a good low-calorie slimming diet, as well as a thorough course of exercise will be very effective. People with this condition should try not to sit down too much or for too long and they should consciously contract the buttock muscles as they walk.

Many women possess what has come to be called the 'shelf' bottom. This is caused by the buttocks forming a distinct shelf of flesh below the lower waist. The common reason for this is

that the sufferer is either standing or walking incorrectly, or both, If an exaggeratedly backward leaning stance is adopted, the bottom is stuck out at the rear to balance this. In this way, the shelf is formed. Any extra flesh on the buttocks will naturally accumulate just below the shelf. This will be even more the case if the same exaggerated leaning back posture is adopted when sitting down.

Posture correction, as well as a thorough course of exercise will go a long way towards improving the shape, if not totally solving the problem. To retain a good figure, and bottoms are an integral part of this, regular exercise,

good posture and a balanced diet are essential. One of the worst things a woman with a beautiful bottom can do is to become complacent. Problems develop through neglect. If they are tackled early they can be rectified; but, if allowed to get worse, the job of cure will be much more difficult.

Whatever shape problem you have with your bottom, exercise and training in posture and stance can be of help. It is important, however, that bad habits are not readopted as soon as the problem appears to go away. The problem can easily reappear and you could be back to square one. Be vigilant and you will keep in shape.

EXERCISE 3
This is a lying down exercise and can be practised in the privacy of your own home. It is very simple to master. This exercise should be done at least once a day to achieve a dramatic improvement in bottom shape. You will need a good bed with a firm mattress.

Lie face down on the bed with your feet together, your hands by your sides and your cheek resting comfortably on the bed cover.

Keeping your left and right legs perfectly straight, raise your left foot as high as is comfortably possible. Hold for a count of one.

Lower slowly. Repeat with the right foot. Try to keep your toes pointed as you raise and lower each foot. Repeat ten times with each foot.

EXERCISE 4

Another exercise that is ideal for indoor practice is the 'walking' exercise. It will help to keep the buttocks firm and rounded.

It can reduce fat and turn what is left into useful muscle once more. Flab often develops on the back of women's thighs. This exercise will help put this right, too. The intention is to attempt to reverse the effects of a largely sedentary life.

Sit on the floor with your back straight. Point your legs straight out in front of you with the feet slightly apart.

Fold your arms comfortably in front of your chest. Now, 'walk' slowly on your buttocks. Continue the walking motion for a count of thirty.

EXERCISE 5

Sit comfortably on your heels, while keeping your back straight.

Raise the arms and grasp wrists above your head.

Raise up slowly to a straight position. Hold this posture for one second.

Lower your bottom slowly until it rests on the floor to the left of your feet. Straighten up again. Now, lower your bottom again. This time it should touch the floor on the right of your feet. Repeat the exercise five times on either side of your feet. This can be increased to ten times for each side as you become more proficient. Practise every day.

It is very important to adopt the correct sitting posture to help keep your bottom in good shape. Whether at work or at home, try to make sure that you sit in a suitable chair. The seat should be of such a height that the knee joint forms a right angle when the feet are resting on the floor. The back of the chair must be a comfortable height and firm enough to support the spine. Sitting down a lot can cause the bottom to become flabby in time. Here are two exercises to help keep the buttock muscles firm even if you have to sit down for most of the time.

EXERCISE 6
Sit upright on the seat with the spine arched backwards slightly. Place your hands on your side at a point just above the hips. A basket or unbreakable bowl should be held between the knees. Now, flex the buttocks while increasing the pressure of the knees on the basket or bowl.

EXERCISE 7
Clasp your hands on the underside of the seat while sitting upright, keep the spine straight. Point your legs straight out in front of you with the feet held firmly together. Slowly, raise your feet from the floor and lower them.

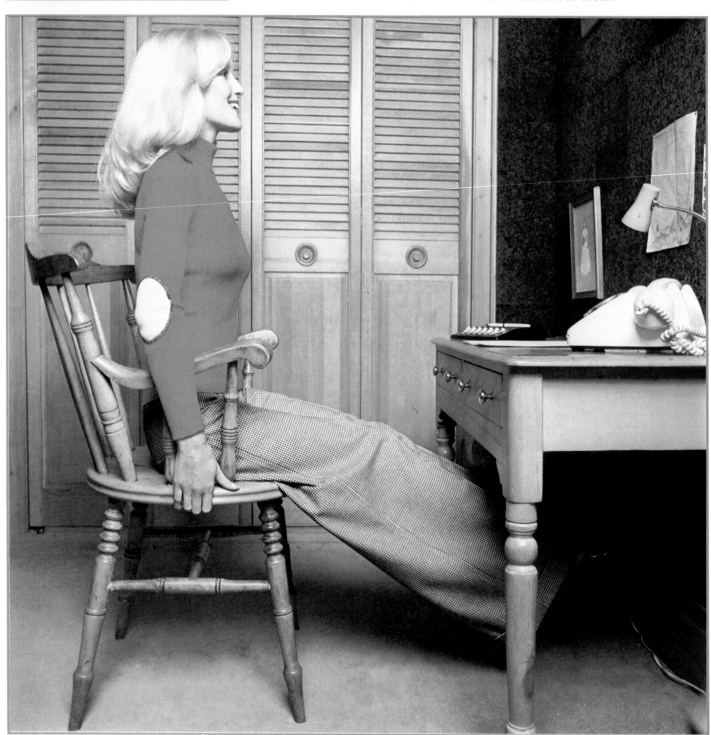

Exercises for the Waist and Midriff

The midriff, the waist and the lower abdomen—frequently and inaccurately referred to as the 'tummy'—are the three regions of the body most susceptible to thickening as a result of accumulations of excess fat. This can occur either because a person eats too much or exercises too little, or a combination of the two. Fortunately, this area between the chest and the hips is also one of the first to respond to any adjustment in diet or increase in exercise.

While a low-calorie diet can help to reduce the amount of stored fat in this region, only exercise can actually tighten up and strengthen the slack muscles. The following exercises are designed to work these muscles gently in order to restore their natural firmness.

When you are exercising, always wear clothes that allow you complete freedom of movement—a bra and pants or a leotard are ideal. This probably means that it will be most convenient to do the exercises either as you get up—which will help to tone you up for the rest of the day—or before you go to bed.

Take advantage of any opportunity to exercise your waist and midriff. Exaggerate all movements—as you dress or climb the stairs, for example—so that you always get the maximum amount of movement around your middle.

Such exercises are suitable for healthy people. If you have any history of back or heart trouble, however, always consult your doctor before you embark on any exercise programme.

If you do these exercises regularly you should soon notice an improvement in the shape and size of your midriff and waist. Such slimness and firmness add a natural grace to your figure that is extremely attractive and will stand you in good stead in later life.

EXERCISE 1

1a. Stand with your feet apart, back straight and your hands clasped behind your head.

1b. Keeping your feet firmly on the ground, twist from the waist upwards round to the right. Return to your original position and twist round to the left.

Repeat 20 times.

Try to be aware of the profile your waist and midriff region is presenting at all times. Do not slouch and stick your 'stomach' out. Instead, stand up straight with your shoulders back and tuck in your seat. You will be able to feel how this lifts your diaphragm and stretches your abdominal muscles, keeping them firm, flat and elegant.

EXERCISE 2

2a. Go down on your hands and knees.

2b. Lift your right leg out to the side, keeping it straight. Make eight forward circles and eight backward circles with your leg. Return to your original position and repeat with your left leg. Repeat this exercise five times with each leg.

1a

2a

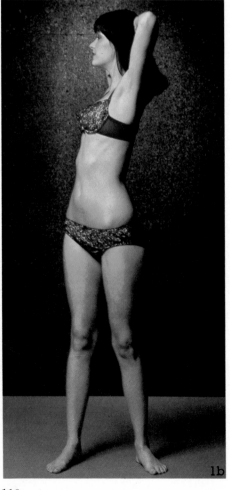

1b

2b

3a

3b

EXERCISE 3

3a. Stand up straight with your shoulders back and feet apart. Stretch your arms high above your head as far as you can reach.

3b. Twist your whole body around to the right as far as you can go, keeping your feet firmly on the ground all the time.

3c. While you are still twisted around, bend and try to grasp your right ankle firmly with both hands. Keep your legs straight throughout. Return to your original position and repeat the movement, this time twisting your whole body around to the left.

Repeat this exercise 20 times.

EXERCISE 4

4a. Sit on the floor with your back perfectly straight, your arms and legs straight out in front of you. Your arms should be held at shoulder height.

4b. Keeping your knees stiff, move forwards on your buttocks by lifting your right leg about six inches from the ground and shifting it forwards as far as it will go. Then repeat the whole movement with your left leg, so that you gradually shuffle forwards. When you have progressed about two feet from your original position, stop and move back to where you started from in the reverse way.

3c

4a

4b

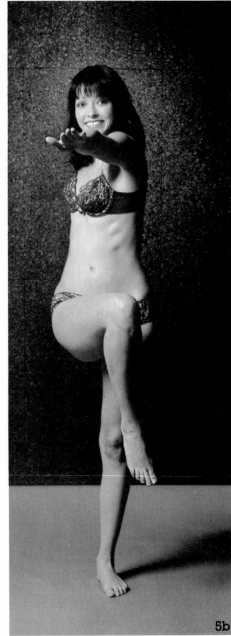

5b

5a

6

EXERCISE 5

5a. Stand with your feet apart and your arms outstretched to the side. Lift your right leg in a high step, so that the sole of your right foot rises above the level of your left knee-cap.

5b. Then swing your right knee across to the left side of your body as far as you can. At the same time, swing your arms in the opposite direction. Swing back to your original position and repeat with your left leg, swinging your arms to the right this time. Repeat this exercise 10 times.

EXERCISE 6

Lie down flat on your back on the floor with your arms straight down beside your body. Raise both your body, arms and feet together, keeping your legs straight, so that your hands touch your toes. Repeat 10 times.

EXERCISE 8

For this exercise you will need a broom.

8a. Hold the broom handle behind your back, level with the small of your back, with the palms of your hands facing inwards. Both your legs should be straight, with one about 18 inches in front of the other.

8b. Twist your body as far as it will go to the right and then to the left.

Repeat eight times in each direction and then change leg positions and repeat for another eight times.

8a

7

8b

EXERCISE 7

Stand up straight with your feet apart and your arms outstretched to the side. Twisting from the waist, bend and touch your left foot with your right hand. Return to your original position and repeat, this time touching your right foot with your left hand. Repeat 10 times.

EXERCISE 9

Again you will need a broom for this exercise.

9a. Stand up straight with your feet together. Clasp the broom handle with both hands and stretch your arms above your head.

9b. Bend gently backwards to a mental count of three.

9c. Then drop your body forwards, bending your knees until the broom is at your feet in front of you. Repeat eight times.

There are other ways of exercising your waist and midriff within your normal range of daily activities. As you are putting on your bra in the morning, for example, stand with your feet apart and, bending forwards from the waist, tip your breasts into the bra cups. Then stand up straight and breathe deeply. When drying your back after a bath, bend your body from side to side from the waist, moving it with your towel as far as you can stretch.

9a

9b

9c

Beauty for all Seasons

The four seasons, spring, summer, autumn and winter, ring in not only changes in temperature but also subtle differences in the way we look and feel. Some people come into their own in the warmer spring and summer months, the sunlight evokes a deep response and they blossom into golden summer people. But others have a less intense response and appear to be marking time until the approach of autumn. It is then that a marked transformation takes place in their approach to personal appearance. These are the winter people who glow in the more chill and sombre atmosphere of colder months.

But what makes us feel at our best at one particular time of year? It may be entirely a question of metabolism or perhaps a deep-seated psychological reason but, whichever it is, most of us

can recognize and claim for our own one of the four seasons. The important thing is to learn how to use the seasonal changes positively to create a beauty image to reflect your personality.

Start with spring, the traditional time for new beginnings. The days grow longer and the sunshine brings limpid clear colours to the fore. If spring is your best time of year you will most probably be one of the first to translate the spring feeling of adventure into a new hairstyle, a fresh feel for summery fabrics and an overall light-hearted approach to life. Now is the time to check up on your figure, weight and measurements. If you are not satisfied with your findings do something positive. Go on a diet. Give up alcohol. Have a health-day once a week or simply have fruit or vegetable juices in place of your usual meal at mid-

day on two days out of seven.

In by-gone days the change of seasons was made all the more dramatic by the ritual celebrations to ensure fertility for summer and a season of ripe fruitfulness for the harvest before winter. Nowadays many of us have a more mundane view of nature and tend to regard the transitions merely as a time to change from heavyweight to lightweight garments. Stop still and take stock. Look at the colours of spring. The transluscent colours of blossoms—pinks, mauves and tangerines—and the delicate green tracery of the trees. How can you use these changes in the natural world to reflect the gay carefree release after winter?

The colours you use in the springtime need to reflect the change from the rich glowing ones of the darker months. The very fact that the intensity of sunlight

increases causes some colours to recede and others to become predominant. New lipstick, new eye colourings and new nail polish will help to bring about a change in your appearance. In place of boldly bright eye shadow try blending two, or even three, shades of the same colour into your own special theme. Blues, greens, lilacs and, if you are dark eyed, the hazel shades will offer excellent opportunities for experiment. Co-ordinate your lipstick and nail polish. They need not be identical, but they should harmonize.

Nails may need a change of shape as well as a change of colour. You could wear them shorter and more rounded at the top for the coming active days of summer. If your nails layer or chip easily after the winter, leave off nail polish for a day or two a week and buff them with a nail cream.

How can your clothes reflect not only the colours and temperature of spring but the increasing exhilaration that one feels on fragile spring evenings? Examine the clothes you have been wearing during the winter and those you had the previous spring. Think of surprising colour combinations and start transforming them.

Some garments may need the hemlines altered. Rather than simply letting down the hem, a novel and imaginative way of lengthening a skirt is to undo the existing hem and make a false one in a contrasting colour and add a matching belt or waistband. Imitation suede on a fine tweed dress can change the look and give a new lease of life to a tired garment. Remove the sleeves of a lightweight winter dress and replace them with hand-knitted crochet ones in a soft yellow, a clear red, or a bright green and link up the colour you choose to a scarf or belt.

Carry this idea of rejuvenating your wardrobe to different kinds of trimming. Examine the possibility of using sequins, fringe, braid or embroidery; creating a false yoke, a waistcoat effect, shoulder emphasis or skirt panels. You can develop this idea of novel trims to the ornaments you can use to lighten the effect of fabrics. Inexpensive bangles in two colours, or simple wood or coloured beads at the neck do wonders to lift a dress out of a rut. If your watch strap is showing signs of wear then rather than going for the conventional black or brown strap, up-date your watch with a colourful strap. Take a look at your shoes and hand-bags—they too can undergo a colour change with the quick and easy paint-on dyes now available.

When you have finished this overhaul turn your attention to your face. Try on your spring clothes and take a look at your hairstyle. There is no better tonic or quicker single way to change your appearance than a trim, cut or colour rinse. Go for a more casual relaxed style than the more tailored look of winter. There are fashions in looks, just as there are in

Spring *time for blossoms and fragile looks*

clothes, so study the styles put forward by top stylists before making your choice. If you are on a budget, remember that a good cut is well worth the money because it not only helps the hair to fall into shape but also it means that it can be washed and better styled at home once you have the basic cut and style.

As the spring advances and the trees take on foliage so you will begin to expose your body to the sun and air. Check on problem skin areas—backs of thighs, knees and elbows. Start regular treatment with a loofah at bathtime and skinfoods or body lotions to keep the circulation in good condition and prevent the skin from drying.

The arrival of summer is heralded by the flowers blooming in myriad hues and the ever-spreading green of the trees. But however much we welcome the radiant colours and strong sunlight, keeping cool in summer can be a problem. Some colours promote a cool feeling —green, yellow, shades of turquoise and blues and the sharp, ice pinks are ideal summer choices. Red and orange tones reflect on the skin and suggest warmth. Cool one-colour garments are kinder to look at than busy patterned ones. Stripes on a crisp white background look summery and cool.

Constricting clothes are those to avoid, particularly if they fit tightly at the waist, or closely beneath the arms. A dress in a fabric such as chiffon or cotton voile can look and feel delightfully fresh on a summer evening. Long sleeves of the wide 'floating' kind are flattering and cool. Easy-care cottons with a man-made fibre additive are recommended for daytime warm weather wear.

Hands and feet that become hot and sticky in summer need attention. Keep hands cool by holding the wrists alternately beneath hot and cold running water. Dry, and spray the palms with deodorant. A two-minute treatment for hot, tired feet is to use a foot-spray on the soles, stroking it between the toes.

The cool way to wear the hair in summer, if it is long, is back from the ears and up from the neck. Tie it with a bright scarf. Have it cut in crisp, short locks on top of the head. Shoulder-length hair can look delightful brushed smooth and worn in a sophisticated version of the ponytail. The summer way with short hair is casual and carefree.

Feet and legs are very much on show during the holiday months and need regular care. Remove unwanted hair with depilatories, wax or electrolysis and use moisturizing lotions or creams to keep the skin smooth and soft. Make a weekly pedicure a summer beauty routine. Varnish toe-nails in rosy hues to give an attractive and natural pink-toed look.

The food you eat plays a big part in the way you feel and look. Include plenty of green vegetables and fresh fruits in your warm-weather diet. Try to include

Summer *time to uncover in sunlit days*

one salad meal a day. But remember you still need proteins, so if you cut down on meat dishes, replace them with more eggs, fish and cheese.

The world is roughly divided into two kinds of women—sun-worshippers and those who cannot wait for cooler days and longer nights. If you come into the second category, autumn will cause your spirits to rise and put a new rhythm in your step and a sparkle in your eyes. The leaves on the trees turn russet and the world is painted in golds, yellows and burnt oranges as the autumn foliage prepares to strip for the dramatic bare effects of winter.

Out go swimsuits and beachwear, sunsuits and cotton dresses, in come 'separates' that can be worn with either woollen or lightweight tops, according to the weather. In come the mix-and-match range of shirts and skirts and slacks and pinafore dresses which mean that for a moderate outlay you can look as if you had a dozen different outfits.

Take a long look at your skin in a good light. Days out of doors, salt water and sunbathing may have left it with a parched, dry look. Use a moisturizing gelée or foam in your bath. Cleanse with a creamy lotion and be generous with skinfood or nourishing cream at night.

Autumn is the time to think about a change of perfume. Change from the light flowery fragrances that go with the fresh, natural look and outdoor days of summer and look for one that is rather more subtle and individual. Enquire about any new perfumes on the market. Skin reaction changes, so it is worth checking on perfumes you have tried out before. They may smell quite different on you from season to season.

The nostalgia and gradually decreasing light of autumn passes swiftly into the bare-branched black and white outlines of winter. Now is the time at which the outside world can provide a stunning foil to the rich colours and fabrics of winter. Winter clothing need never be dull or drab. Winter is the time when your imagination and flair can come into their own. One look backwards at the magnificence of by-gone fashions is proof enough—the elegant capes trimmed with velvets or fur, the use to which black and autumn russets were put.

One of the best ways of keeping your spirits from flagging and being overwhelmed by the grey evenings and overcast days is to maintain the reserve of energy and fitness gained in the summer months. Try to take more exercise; to spend more time out of doors, to carry on with some activity you followed in the holiday months such as swimming, tennis or walking. Join a yoga class or start simple exercise sessions.

A healthy, glowing look is the keynote to winter beauty. Look as if you are enjoying the crisp cold weather and you will be halfway towards doing so. This

Autumn *time of contrast and mists*

means you must be dressed for the part. Wrists, feet, and neck especially should be kept warm. Wear a woolly cap, a fake-fur helmet or a scarf to protect the head and ears when the temperature drops and the cold winds of winter begin to blow. Several layers of thinner clothing will give you more protection and conserve body heat better than a single garment.

Sudden changes of temperature are bad for the skin. So do not go out into the cold immediately after washing the face or downing a hot drink—or an alcoholic one. Keep your skin nourished and avoid huddling too close to radiators or open fires.

Towards mid-winter, stodgy foods, stuffy rooms and heavier make-up often make the skin look tired and dull. A cut orange rubbed lightly over a clean face two or three times a week is an easy routine to tone and freshen the skin. A herbal or cucumber face mask used every two or three weeks helps to remove any impurities and clear away blemishes. It also improves the texture of the skin and fines the pores.

If you suffer from cold hands, a thirty-second shake-up every now and again during the day is a good way to get the circulation going. With elbows at your sides, and arms held upwards, shake hands vigorously to and fro, allowing them to hang limp from the wrists.

If cold feet are a problem, do not wear tight shoes; even changing over to thicker stockings with the same size footwear can mean that the feet do not get enough breathing space. Promote the flow of blood to feet by sitting on a chair with your shoes off and your toes pointing towards the floor. Now, with the foot as limp as possible—this improves with practice—swing it loosely to and fro from the ankle. Draw up the toes and try to arch the underside of the foot to make a 'hens foot'. Release and extend the toes as far out as possible. Repeat three times with each foot.

Warm, vibrant colours help to emphasize the glowing winter look. You will feel warm when you look warm. Do not overlook the clever things that can be done with costume jewellery. Coral, garnet, topaz, deep purple and old gold all have a rich glow about them. Colours we think of as cool, such as turquoise, pale green, or amber, worn at the neck of a dark dress or sweater will lighten and brighten it and effectively soften winter garments.

Whatever the season, if you take the time and trouble to follow the various beauty routines described in this book you will be more than pleased with the results. No woman is perfect but by the same token there is no woman without at least one special feature which she wants to accentuate. In dealing with the figure bit by bit we have set out to tell a woman everything she needs to know about making herself more beautiful.

Winter *time for fantasy and furs*

Index